MW01060229

FAMINE

NEW PERSPECTIVES ON THE PAST

General Editor
R. I. Moore

Advisory Editors
Gerald Aylmer
Tanya Luhrmann
David Turley
Patrick Wormald

PUBLISHED

IN PREPARATION

FAMINE

SOCIAL CRISIS AND HISTORICAL CHANGE

David Arnold

Basil Blackwell

Basil Blackwell Ltd
108 Cowley Road, Oxford OX4 1JF, UK

Basil Blackwell Inc.
432 Park Avenue South, Suite 1503
New York, NY 10016, USA

British Library Cataloguing in Publication Data

Arnold, David,
Famine.
1. Famines, to 1988
I. Title
363.8

ISBN 0-631-15118-4
ISBN 0-631-15119-2 Pbk

Library of Congress Cataloging in Publication Data

Arnold, David (David J.)
Famine.

(New perspectives on the past)
Bibliography: p.
Includes index.
1. Famines. I. Title. II. Series.
HC79.F3A76 1988   363.8   88-22133
ISBN 0-631-15118-4
ISBN 0-631-15119-2 (pbk.)

Typeset in 11 on 13pt Plantin
by Downdell Ltd., Abingdon, Oxon.
Printed in Great Britain by
Billing & Sons Ltd, Worcester

Contents

Editor's Preface

Ignorance has many forms, and all of them are dangerous. In the nineteenth and twentieth centuries our chief effort has been to free ourselves from tradition and superstition in large questions, and from the error in small ones upon which they rest, by redefining the fields of knowledge and evolving in each the distinctive method appropriate for its cultivation. The achievement has been incalculable, but not without cost. As each new subject has developed a specialist vocabulary to permit rapid and precise reference to its own common and rapidly growing stock of ideas and discoveries, and come to require a greater depth of expertise from its specialists, scholars have been cut off by their own erudition not only from mankind at large, but from the findings of workers in other fields, and even in other parts of their own. Isolation diminishes not only the usefulness but the soundness of their labours when energies are exclusively devoted to eliminating the small blemishes so embarrassingly obvious to the fellow-professional on the next patch, instead of avoiding others that may loom much larger from, as it were, a more distant vantage point. Marc Bloch observed a contradiction in the attitudes of many historians: 'when it is a question of ascertaining whether or not some human act has really taken place, they cannot be too painstaking. If they proceed to the reasons for that act, they are content with the merest appearance, ordinarily founded upon one of those maxims of common-place psychology which are neither more nor less true that their opposites.' When the historian peeps across the fence he sees his neighbours, in literature, perhaps, or sociology, just as complacent in relying on historical platitudes which are naive, simplistic or obsolete.

New Perspectives on the Past represents not a reaction against specialization, which would be a romantic absurdity, but an attempt to come to terms with it. The authors, of course, are specialists, and their thought and conclusions rest on the foundation of distinguished professional research in different periods and fields. Here they will free themselves, as far as it is possible, from the restraints of subject, region and period within which they ordinarily and necessarily work, to discuss problems simply as problems, and not as 'history' or 'politics' or 'economics'. They will write for specialists, because we are all specialists now, and for laymen, because we are all laymen.

We must eat. In consequence of the simplest of all imperatives famine is both a subject of urgent contemporary concern and one which casts a harsh and clear light on the nature and problems of the societies it afflicts and of the world in which they exist. It has been and remains at the centre of the great turning points in world history, in social and economic structures and in human relations. Its terrifying fascination is no less obvious than its fundamental importance. Yet it is not difficult to understand why famine has been very little studied as a phenomenon in its own right: the questions it raises are complex and often obscure, and the contemplation of the great mass of evidence with which they are to be answered, from every age and every continent, is a baffling and desperately depressing business. But they are elementary questions in the fullest sense, plunging to the foundations of power and social organization. In David Arnold's hands they show how disciplined scholarship, clarity of thought and style, and human passion can live together, and remind us forcefully that the understanding of the part cannot be separated from that of the whole, or the understanding of the present from that of the past.

R.I. Moore

Foreword

Famine is far from being a novel subject for the historian. The historical texts of antiquity bear witness to famine as being one of the oldest and most traumatic trials of men, just as the history of our own times continues to be punctuated by famine and a fear of famine. The last few decades have seen a remarkable scholarly outpouring and multi-disciplinary debate on the causes, character and consequences of mass hunger. This has been prompted in part by the famines of the 1970s and 1980s in the Sahel and Ethiopia and the public concern they have generated, but also by a growing sensitivity to the ecological precariousness of our planet, to which the persistence of famine into the modern age seems to give grim testimony, and by the realization among historians and demographers alike that famine ruled the populations of the past in a manner more ruthless and relentless than scholars had hitherto assumed. But, in the main, historians have confined themselves to analyzing the complexities of a single famine episode (however much they seek to suggest its wider ramifications and to offer parallels with other times of dearth and hunger), or they have been content to incorporate famine into their work as merely a facet or phase of their wider historical explorations. It has often been left, therefore, to the non-historian to speculate upon the more general place of famine in human experience.

So much has been written about famine in recent years that it might reasonably be doubted whether there was anything left to say. I think there is, and especially from an historical perspective. While, I hope, learning and benefiting from other disciplines, I have tried to retrieve the broad historical significance of famine, to see it as a phenomenon of importance not only as an individual episode or 'event' (of value for what it can reveal about a given society at a particular moment in time), but also as a marker or accelerator of historical change in the longer term. My intention has been (probably to the despair of the regional specialist and the cultural purist) to seek out the wider, even global, significance of famine, as a point of contact (or area of confusion) between different societies and cultures as well as the occasion for deep division and bitter conflict within societies. My aim has been to represent famine not only in its familiar guise as demographic catastrophe and economic malaise but also as a phenomenon of far-reaching political, social and cultural importance as well.

Without Bob Moore's invitation it is unlikely that this book would have been conceived, let alone written. I am grateful to him for asking me to write it and for his help and encouragement along the way. I have benefited, too, from the suggestions and advice of several colleagues at Lancaster University and owe a particular word of thanks to John MacKenzie, and to Lee Beier for his help with chapter 5. But, as befits a general work of this kind, I have long-standing debts to acknowledge, too – to Christopher Platt, who twenty years ago impressed on me the desirability of studying famine and did much more besides to nurture my wider historical interests; to Anthony Low for his continuing encouragement and enthusiasm for a comparative approach to the history of the extra-European world; and to Ranajit Guha and the 'Subaltern Studies' crowd for the continuing stimulation of the 'subaltern' approach to history (and with a particular word of thanks to David Hardiman for his comments on an earlier draft). I would like to thank, too, Virginia Murphy and Carol Ann Busia for their considerable help in seeing the manuscript through the press. And finally, my warmest thanks to Juliet Miller – for encouragement, insight and understanding over a great many years.

David Arnold
January, 1988

Introduction

The history of man from the beginning has been the history of his struggle for daily bread
                    Josué de Castro *The Geopolitics of Hunger*, p. 49

The recent famines in Africa and the continuing threat of mass starvation in many parts of Asia and Latin America serve to remind us that famine is more than just an historical phenomenon. It continues to stalk the Third World today as it once did Europe in an earlier, pre-industrial age. Although for most people in the present-day western world famine is a distant hunger, more Old Testament than contemporary in its images and resonances, the prospect of famine on a massive, possibly global, scale still haunts our collective fears and imagination. The Malthusian spectre of a hungry and overcrowded planet lurks somewhere in almost any discussion, scholarly or lay, about population growth or Third World poverty and development. For all our technology, for all our food mountains, for all our apparent security from absolute want and starvation, famine remains an apocalyptic vision for our time as much as for the hungry ages of the past.

The persistence of mass hunger in the contemporary world has inevitably begged questions of the past as well as the present. Are the famines of today intrinsically different from those of previous centuries? Does history confirm or refute a Malthusian prognosis? What are the historical roots of famine in Africa today? Are there historical reasons why some parts of the globe appear to be more famine-prone than others? Why has famine become a Third World phenomenon?

Interestingly enough, it is more often demographers and economists, geographers, anthropologists and political scientists, rather than historians, who have made the running in the recent discussion of famine and who have advanced many of the most challenging theories. The value of this for historians is that they can profit from the insights and specialist knowledge of other disciplines and gain a broader understanding of a phenomenon that is clearly too complex and far-reaching to remain the province of one discipline alone. But there are drawbacks, too. Scholars operating from other disciplinary bases often shed no light on the issues that are foremost in the historian's mind or they happily harbour presumptions and prejudices that the discerning historian will rightly baulk at. Some treat history as little more than a series of anecdotal asides. Others seem to regard it as merely a painted backdrop, a museum diorama, without the animation to breathe life into the vistas of the past. The past exists merely to echo the present.

For their own part, historians, wary of generalizing over such a vast terrain, have preferred the familiar confines of a single famine to a sweeping comparative phenomenology of famine. They have been anxious to stress the specificity as well as the complexity, the uniqueness rather than the universality, of any given famine episode. The superficial physical similarities between one famine and another, which are often what strike casual observers most forcefully (as if all famine 'victims' were reduced to a single timeless anonymity of destitution and misery), are treated by many historians these days with great caution and are taken to conceal enormous and ineluctable differences between one society or one age and another. Famine in Imperial China, say, or nineteenth-century India is seen to be the outcome of vastly different political institutions, social processes and economic structures from famine in contemporary Ethiopia or the Sahel. This is reasonable enough, but the task of the historian then appears to be little more than to cautiously endorse or stubbornly reprove the theorizing of the brasher disciplines rather than to speculate on famine's wider historical character and meaning.

And yet in a singular way famine is, or should be, of particular moment to the history-making of our times. This is not just because the famines of the past may (or, of course, may not) be, in the layman's favoured phrase, 'relevant', and tell us much about the causes of today's mass hunger and the historical antecedents of the current division of the world between the starving poor and the stinking rich. It is also that the history of hunger and all those related issues that buzz about it like swarming bees – what food people ate and how this varied from class to class or from one age to another, how families shared out the food available to them, the social and economic relations that were tested in times of dearth and stress, the crime, the migrations, the rebellions, and all the myriad forms of social and cultural adaptation that hunger gave birth to – is critically central to the new social history. Individually and collectively these diverse aspects of human existence and interaction enrich and enlarge our understanding of life in the past tense. They offer an escape from the history of kings and countries to the history of people and persons.

For historians with an interest in the material conditions, ideas and social relations of the subordinate classes or of the family, an episode such as a famine can provide a rare glimpse of the lives of the 'common people', and shed light on matters of everyday significance about which historical source materials are all too often silent. Only perhaps at times such as these are we able to learn what (and how much) a peasant household had to eat, the nature of popular religious beliefs (in contrast, perhaps, to the well-documented doctrines of the orthodox priesthood), and the expectations which the 'common people' had of their landlords and the state. In times of famine the suffering of the poor was too monumental, and their collective behaviour of too great an economic and political significance, for kings, courtiers and colonial bureaucrats simply to ignore. Famine opens up to our understanding at least a fragment of the historical experience of subordinate social groups and of their interactions with the state and elites that would otherwise remain lost to us.

All this might make of history nothing more than an antiquarian cookbook with crumbling pages and quaint recipes or an old-fashioned cabinet of curiosities – full of interest but devoid of purpose – were it not that social history is no longer, as G. M. Trevelyan once described it, 'history with the politics left out'. It is propelled not just by a curiosity about the past but also by a discreet passion, by a sensitivity to the political nuances and the political structures of everyday life. It is alert to the ways in which power – politics in the broadest sense – was exercised over and within a given community.

As this book will briefly try to show, historically food was one of the principal sinews of power. Its importance was felt at all levels of society, both by those who suffered directly for want of basic sustenance and those whose authority, security and profit were threatened as the indirect consequence of dearth and mass starvation – from the family to the state, from the peasant households of medieval Europe or Imperial China to the colonial empires of the nineteenth century and the international market economy of the present day. Food was, and continues to be, power in a most basic, tangible and inescapable form. To a degree to which we in the well-fed world have perhaps ceased actively to acknowledge, food was not only essential for the maintenance of human life and bodily activity, but was also fundamental to the structures of dominance and dependency that arose out of this most vital of all commodities. Food (and the denial or absence of food that famine entailed) was (and remains even in a relatively secure and secularized society like our own) richly symbolic, a potent and recurrent motif in the semantics of kingship and statecraft, in the language and imagery of religion and culture. In talking about food and famine, therefore, we are not picking at the margins of historical experience or tracking the rare trajectory of a Halley's comet across the historical firmament. We are dealing with the very stuff of history.

But there is no denying the almost bewildering breadth of famine as a historical subject, one not easily compressed within such narrow confines as these. I have elected, therefore, to narrow most of the discussion that follows to the significance of famine in peasant societies. There is an element of historical convenience in this. We know more about famines in peasant societies than in the forms of social organization that preceded or paralleled them, among hunter-gatherers, for example, or among nomadic pastoralists, if only because peasants generally formed part of literate societies able to record the occurrence and impact of famines. And though scholars may quibble over the exact identity of peasants and peasantries, there seems to me enough broad agreement for the concept to be of general utility in trying to bring together for comment an array of societies otherwise separated by time and space, by geography and culture, and by the scholarly division of labour. But, as I shall try to demonstrate, famine has also had a particularly intimate, indeed structural, relationship with peasant societies, and so, by deepening our understanding of the one, we can hope to gain a greater appreciation of the meaning and impact of the other. Peasants serve, too, as a common medium through which to link the context and the experience of famine in Europe with famine in the colonial world of the nineteenth and twentieth centuries and in those parts of Asia, Africa and Latin America we have come to call the Third World. Through the peasant medium we can begin to understand how the impact of colonialism increased famine vulnerability over half the inhabited globe while, through the peasants' destruction or absence, the western world of Europe and North America was able in recent times to free itself from the perennial scourge of mass starvation.

1
Definitions and Dimensions

Famines are woven into the fabric of history. We have become accustomed to thinking of them as 'disasters' of a particularly horrific kind, replete with human misery on a massive, almost unimaginable, scale. Disasters and catastrophes famines undoubtedly are, and in that lies part, but by no means all, of their historical significance. Through their sheer magnitude and through the extent of the devastation and disruption they cause, famines have been powerful engines of historical transformation, driving some societies to the verge of extinction, impelling others into wholesale migration or radical economic, political and social change. The persistent fear of hunger, the recurrent threat of starvation, reinforced by the periodic visitations of famine itself, have profoundly influenced human society throughout the ages and helped fashion elaborate strategies for survival, subsistence and collective security. The near universality of dearth and famine has given poignancy of meaning to idylls of paradise and plenty, just as the spectre of mass starvation has further darkened the apprehensions and experiences of warfare and invasion, of droughts, floods and epidemics. Famine rides out with Pestilence, with Death and Destruction, and the sound of their passing hooves is echoed in the anxious prayer:

> From lightning and tempest; from plague, pestilence and famine; from battle and murder, and from sudden death, Good Lord, deliver us.

Famine affects the way in which we view the past - challenging cosy assumptions about some lost golden age of abundance and ease - and influences the ways in which we perceive the hazards of our collective future. It has been one of the most potent and formative influences in our understanding of the modern world and of its searing division between the rich nations and the poor. Famine is one of the most powerful, pervasive, and arguably one of the most emotive, words in our historical vocabulary, and that in itself makes it all the more difficult to isolate its meaning and wider significance.

Event and structure

One of the problems with famine – as a concept and as an historical phenomenon – is that it presents us with a fundamental paradox. It is both event and structure. On the one hand it is clearly an 'event'. There may be widely differing opinions as to when exactly a particular famine began or ended, but there will be common agreement that it occupied a finite span of historical time and human experience. A famine is also an 'event' in the sense of being an exceptional episode standing apart from the course of the everyday life that surrounds it. In some regards famine represents the negation of all that is normal and familiar: in the desperation of their hunger people turn to unfamiliar or forbidden foods; homes and fields are deserted; families disintegrate; wives and children are abandoned or sold into slavery or prostitution; the corpses of the dead choke the rivers or lie unburied in the streets. Individually, one or other of these attributes might be found in a society or in part of a society even at the best of times and certainly in many a hard year. But taken together and sequentially they add up to a collective crisis exceptional in its scale and intensity. The exceptionality of famine is part of its distinctive character.

Even in the most impoverished societies, famines are not everyday occurrences, and definitions that equate famine with 'severe mal-nutrition', 'acute food shortages', or even 'extreme hunger', while identifying some of the salient aspects of the famine situation, fall short of capturing its totality; they fail to convey the urgency and abhorrence, the sense of crisis and despair. However nutritionists may seek to define and quantify it, famine connotes more than a shortfall in individual nutritional needs and daily calorific intake. It has, anyway, in practice proved very difficult to set universal standards for daily minimum food or calorific requirements, and deficiencies in diet and nutrition exist permanently or are seasonally recurrent in many societies, past and present, even in supposedly 'normal' times. As the official enquiry into the Bengal famine of 1943–44 pointed out, even in years of good harvests only 22 per cent of Bengal's population could be said to be 'well-nourished' while, even without a famine to depress food consumption still further, 31 per cent were 'very badly nourished'. Nutritional levels alone cannot define a famine.

Famine signifies an exceptional (if periodically recurring) event, a collective catastrophe of such magnitude as to cause social and economic dislocation. It generally results in abnormal levels of desti-tution, hunger and death. It can lead to the complete disintegration of customary patterns of work and subsistence and can greatly disrupt customary norms of morality and social behaviour. If hunger can be likened to disease, famine constitutes its epidemic rather than endemic state, the multiplication of existing conditions of inequality, poverty and malnutrition into a crisis of massive proportions.

And yet, at the same time, famine is rarely a bolt from the blue, a wholly random and unpredictable occurrence that can be meaningfully considered in isolation from the economic, social, and political structures of a specific society. There are, of course, instances of localized famine conditions resulting from a flash flood or earthquake, or the cutting off of a city or country under siege from its usual food supplies, and in such cases there may not be structural causes and long-term antecedents. Europe's most recent experiences of mass hunger – the Paris Commune of 1871, the blockade of Germany in the later stages of the First World War, the siege of Leningrad in 1942–43, and the Dutch winter of hunger in 1944–45 – were essentially of this kind, affecting societies that were otherwise relatively secure in their food provisioning. More commonly, however, famine acts as a revealing commentary upon a society's deeper and more enduring difficulties. The proximate cause of a famine might lie in some apparently unpredictable 'natural disaster', like a flood or drought, or in a 'man-made' calamity like a civil war or invasion; but these are often no more than the precipitating factors, intensifying or bringing to the fore a society's inner contradictions and inherent weaknesses, exposing an already extant vulnerability to food shortages and famine. Some societies are sufficiently resilient to shake off the effects of a drought or flood without suffering much hardship or loss of life, while others, subjected to a similar experience, are almost overwhelmed by mass starvation and high mortality. As Guy Bois puts it, 'the effects of external attack are generally a function of the attacked'. The human consequences of a cyclone in Bangladesh are immeasurably greater than those of a cyclone pounding the Florida coast – not because the nature of the cyclone is inherently different but because some societies are infinitely more vulnerable to the effects of famine and natural disaster than others. Thus although famine has meaning and context as an 'event' in itself, distinguishable from what precedes and follows it, it is seldom an entirely isolated episode or a purely chance misfortune. As in Russia or China on the eve of their revolutionary upheavals, a famine can be a symptom of the deeper malaise affecting a corrupt polity and a decaying social order; and, in its turn, it can help to propel that society further towards a climactic denouement. Nor is the underlying cause and outcome of the crisis necessarily of a purely social and political character. It can also, as we have grown increasingly aware, reflect a long-term process of environmental degradation, an imbalance between man and nature brought about by increasing pressure on the land or by the careless misuse and over-exploitation of natural resources. Here, too, the drought or the civil war that marks the onset of famine may be only the precipitating cause of a crisis long brewing.

Equally, although what happens during the course of a famine will bear many signs of abnormality, it will also continue to some degree to be shaped by pre-existing cultural norms and social relations. For example, customary taboos or prejudices against the eating of certain foodstuffs may not be overthrown even when individuals are confronted with the direst hunger. Caste Hindus in India's nineteenth-century famines could not be persuaded to abandon their customary religious opposition to eating beef (despite the abundance of cattle till they too perished from thirst and hunger) nor, in many cases, would they accept food prepared by low-caste cooks at relief works and charitable food centres since this, too, ran counter to caste prohibitions. Food did not lose its sacred or sacrilegious connotations just because there was a famine, though when transgressions of normal taboos did occur, it further enhanced the sense of abhorrence and abnormality that famine represented in the minds of those who suffered and witnessed it. Although one cannot but be struck by the apparent universality of many aspects of famine behaviour – the recourse to 'famine foods', for instance, or to migration – the precise character of the reactions involved and their local significance bear the imprint of a society's distinctive cultural and social forms.

However unexpected, however devastating the crisis, a society will not act entirely out of character during a famine. Indeed people may cling all the more resolutely to the cultural and social wreckage of their former lives to sustain them through such tragedies and traumas. The catastrophe itself was often explained in terms of existing religious beliefs and millennarian prophesies, just as those affected sought to end or ameliorate it through appropriate prayers and rituals. Likewise, the manner of the state's response varied according to the nature of its pre-existing conventions and ideology quite as much as its administrative capabilities and financial resources. Any historical understanding of famine must therefore be alert to its structural causes and its social and cultural parameters as well as to what happened during the crisis itself.

In approaching famine in this way, as a meeting and intermingling of event and structure, we are touching upon more than the question of what constitutes a famine. Since the Second World War famine has become a critical part of historical and demographic discussion about the nature of society in the pre-modern and early modern world. Pioneering scholars like Jean Meuvret and Pierre Goubert in France identified and documented through a wealth of statistical data and circumstantial evidence the existence of recurrent 'subsistence crises' during which food prices soared far above normal levels (and thus way beyond the capacity of the mass of the people to afford), epidemics (sometimes spurred on by invasion and warfare) raged among a famished population, mortality rates doubled or trebled while the birth rate faltered and slumped. These periodic crises have come to be seen as one of the characteristic hallmarks of society under Europe's *ancien régime* and as major checks upon population growth and economic prosperity until at least the eighteenth century.

Following the lead of Meuvret and Goubert, other scholars, again particularly in France, have applied similar techniques and approaches to other societies, too, or have elaborated upon the impact of these crises on the social framework and political fabric of the European past. In particular, Fernand Braudel, Emmanuel Le Roy Ladurie, and other members of what has broadly become known as the 'Annales school', have railed against the idea of history as simply a narrative sequence of 'great events and great personalities' (dismissed by Braudel as constituting mere 'surface disturbances'), towards a history of underlying structures and recurrent patterns – subsistence crises among them. The sea-changes that occur in human society in the long-term (Braudel's now celebrated *longue durée*) are seen to be of far greater historical moment than the deliberations of kings, the intrigues of priests and princes or the wars and revolutions that figured so prominently in the history writing of an earlier time. Reacting in part, too, to the constraints and conventions of Marxist historiography (at least of an old-fashioned variety), with its economic determinism and dialectical materialism, the Annalistes have looked instead, if not to an environmental determinism, then at least to a long-term interaction between man and nature, a dialectic, as Braudel conceived it, between space and time, geography and history, observable over the *longue durée* but barely perceptible in the short run. In their pursuit of a 'total history', historians of the Annales school have initiated fruitful exchanges with many other disciplines, especially demography. One of their most valuable contributions has been to investigate the historical importance of climatic change and the cycle of seasons and harvests and to discover the consequences these had for agriculture, settlement and trade, the movement of food prices, population trends,

and the periodicity and dissemination of epidemic disease – all matters
having a bearing, directly or indirectly, upon famine.

In a characteristically ambitious work, Le Roy Ladurie in *The
Peasants of Languedoc* wove a discussion of famine into a wide-ranging
survey of an entire cycle of French agrarian history, beginning with
recovery from the Black Death of the fourteenth century, through
a period of prosperity and agricultural expansion and back to a
bleakly Malthusian denouement in famine and epidemic disease. The
emphasis is thus not upon famine as a self-contained episode, but as
one of the characteristic features of the long-term trends and recurrent
demographic, agrarian and social patterns of the pre-industrial age.
However, Le Roy Ladurie has not always shown himself to be entirely
comfortable with the *longue durée* and the structuralist approach to
history. In reviewing Pierre Goubert's work on the Beauvais region of
northern France in the seventeenth and eighteenth century, first
published in 1960, Le Roy Ladurie duly noted the area's frequent
famines and serious food shortages as one of the identifying marks of
the age, but then went on to express reservations about too narrow an
interpretation of their historical significance:

> such 'events' [he wrote] are mentioned by Goubert only in order to
> stress what surrounded them, to place them within a recurrent structure
> which regularly brings round, by virtue of a universally applicable
> concept, the inevitable 'subsistence crisis' – itself accompanied by a
> series of typical, negative and quantifiable characteristics: high cereal
> prices; high mortality rates among the poor through nutrition and
> among the rich through epidemics; a decline in the number of
> marriages, which are postponed until better days; [and] the temporary
> barrenness of women who are normally fertile, whether as a result of
> amenorrhea caused by famine or for other reasons.[1]

Through his own more recent work, such as the study of the village
of Montaillou or the Carnival at Romans in 1579–80, Le Roy Ladurie
has shown further doubts about an exclusive reliance upon an
approach to history which tends to drain individual events of their
specific character and signficance and which threatens to swallow up
human actors and human ideas in a vast swirling ocean of time and
space. Even an event of the historical magnitude of the Black Death,
which robbed Europe of a third of its population within a matter of
months, can be reduced to relative insignificance if the perspective is
sufficiently distant and all-encompassing. Other critics, too, have

---

1. Le Roy Ladurie, *The Territory of the Historian*, p. 112.

pointed out the pitfalls of an overly reductionist approach, which squeezes out of history many of the very things that are most meaningful to it and reduces it to a circus of structures, cycles and conjunctures in which the historian alone can play ring-master. Moreover, in positing a dialectic only between man and nature there is a risk of making men and women merely passive spectators of 'natural' forces, like droughts and epidemics, over which they seemingly have no control, are powerless to resist, and so can know only as 'victims'. As the French Marxist historian Jean Chesneaux pointed out, this 'massive' history can readily become a passive history and an apparently apolitical one with the story of human struggle, inventiveness, oppression and resistance simply left out. Such an approach has little to say about the experience and the consciousness of the people and the ways in which this informed their responses to their material conditions and socio-political environment. What to people at the time was an overwhelming calamity, an experience of immense significance in their own lives, is casually treated as a mere 'surface disturbance' or as something too short-term and cyclical to merit further investigation. An historical approach to famine obviously needs to examine the importance of long-term and structural determinants and to be able to fit a specific famine within the wider historical context. But at the same time it should not lose sight of the famine's character as a distinctive episode, charged with political and cultural meaning, and itself capable of quickening the pace or altering the direction of historical change.

Famines as history

Famines are important historical markers, and have often been used as such by chroniclers and historians in search of moments in time when the normal rhythms of human life were interrupted, or when momentous developments appeared to have a discernible beginning or end. The 'Great Hunger' of the 1840s, for example, has often been taken to mark a major watershed in the history of Ireland and the Irish people. Joel Mokyr in his recent study *Why Ireland Starved*, confidently asserts that the famine

> completely altered the course of Irish history, left an indelible mark on the mentality, attitudes, and beliefs of the Irish, and made Ireland into a demographic anomaly which singles it out as *sui generis* in modern European history.

And though some historians these days would be more cautious in attributing quite so much to the famine itself, most still accept that it had far-reaching and enduring effects on matters as diverse as marriage, migration, land-use and agrarian relations.

In singling out famines in this way historians have done rather more than just seize upon convenient dates by which to slice up the seemingly indivisible course of history into more manageable portions. They have also, as the Irish case clearly exemplifies, followed the perceptions and traditions of the people themselves. In pre-literate societies in particular famines served along with other collective catastrophes as a common means of recording and recovering the experience of the past. The occurrence of other events of personal or public significance have often been recalled in oral tradition by locating them in relation to the date of a particular famine, which acts as the pole around which all other experiences and impressions are organized and collected. Famine thus forms a link between the world of personal memory and the broader domain of collective consciousness.

It has been remarked, for instance, in India, both in connection with the major famines of the nineteenth century and the Bengal famine of 1943–44, how peasants used these traumatic episodes as personal reference points to tell their ages or to recall other dates and events. It was said of the people of Aligarh district in northern India that not only did they long remember the famine of 1837 for its severity and the hardship it caused; it was also the point from which the poorer classed reckoned time, and to which they related all their misfortunes. Henry Morris in his account of the Godavari district in south India, published in the 1870s, remarked that he had often asked men their age and they had been unable to tell him. The only way to determine their age was to ask how old they had been at the time of the 'Great Famine' of 1833, which, through its heavy mortality, had left a lasting impression upon personal and collective memory. As an aid to their recall, as a reminder of their terrifying consequences, and, sometimes, as a key to their putative meaning, famines were given particular names. The practice of naming famines is, incidentally, one indication that in the popular memory at least all famines were far from being identical whatever similarities they might hold for outside observers. India's famines commonly bore the title of the year in the Hindu calendar in which they occurred. The Gujarat famine of 1899 was known locally as 'Chappen' (fifty-six) because it fell in the year 1956 of the Samvat era, while an earlier one, long remembered as 'Ignothare' after the Samvat year 1869 (AD 1813), 'became a household word, signifying a great famine'. Others, however, were named after vengeful deities or were seen as marking the onset of the Kali Yuga, the Hindu age of suffering, corruption and human misery. One particularly widespread and destructive Indian famine in the four-teenth century was recalled for generations afterwards as Durgadevi after the awesome Hindu goddess of this name.

African famines also bore descriptive titles that chronicled for future generations the episode's tragic features and the dire expedients to which people were reduced by their destitution and hunger. One pre-colonial famine in Niger was named after the sale of children, another after the water gourds that were ground up for food. The severe and widespread Sahelian drought of 1913-14 was remembered locally by the characteristic 'barrel-bellies' of the starving. The year 1931 was the 'year of the locust larvae' that devoured the standing crops. Even more grimly, a famine in western Niger in 1942 became known as Wande-Maasu, recalling the way in which hunger drove men to cast off their wives. The famines of central Tanzania were labelled in a similar fashion. One, around 1850, was known to the Gogo as Chonya-Magulu, that is, the time when, crippled by the effects of hunger and malnutrition, people could only hobble about; another in 1885 was called Chilemu, after the time when villagers deserted their homes and migrated elsewhere in search of food; a third in about 1870, Mamudemu, apparently referred to the 'bursting of the intestines' of those who had eaten indigestible 'famine foods'.

Preserved in the main through oral tradition, the recollection of such famines provided the people of Africa and India with a historical almanac of their own, one that often had more meaning to their own lives than royal genealogies and priestly chronicles. Some, remarkably, served as historical markers spanning several centuries and, indeed, they have begun to be used by historians to confirm or establish the chronology of other events such as migrations and invasions as far back as the fourteenth and fifteenth centuries.

But some famines were so severe and protracted, so reeked of human disaster, that further description and elaboration was not needed to prompt their recall. They were simply - as in Portugal in 1521, in England in 1594-96, in Russia in 1601-03, or in Ireland in 1846-51 - '*the* Famine' or 'the Great Hunger'. Even the words 'hunger', 'drought' or 'famine' might themselves be enough decades after the event to spark a train of bitter recall. 'When a Brazilian hears one speak of "drought"', observed the sociologist Gilberto Freyre in 1948, 'he thinks immediately of Ceará' – the area of northeastern Brazil where in 1877 an estimated 500,000 people perished from hunger and disease – 'and '77. One place and one date.'

The subject of folklore and legend, the counterpoint to tales of wise kings and benevolent gods, famines formed, too, an integral part of more formal attempts to record and recall the past. In the 1870s when Cornelius Walford set out to compile a comprehensive list of the world's famines he drew heavily on medieval and early modern European chronicles; and at about the same date British officials in India and China tried to make similar inventories using indigenous accounts. That they were able to do so was indicative of the prominence afforded to famine (and to other 'disasters') in the historical annals of those civilizations. In 1878 a British consular official in China, Alexander Hosie, compiled a list of famines in China from AD 620 to 1643: his principal source was the *T'u-shu chi ch'eng*, a compendium of earlier records prepared for the Emperor K'ang Hi in the first half of the eighteenth century. Later writers have uncovered even more extensive materials for China covering some two thousand famines between the third century BC and the fall of the last imperial dynasty, the Manchus, in the revolution of 1911. The preservation of records relating to famine, as well as to drought, flood, and other catastrophes, over such a vast period of time testifies to the way in which Chinese history has been constantly punctuated by episodes of this kind. But (and it is a point to which I shall return in a later chapter) it is indicative, too, of the political significance China's rulers attached to the occurrence of calamities apparently so pregnant with meaning.

Historians of medieval Europe have been surprisingly sceptical about the authenticity and reliability of the accounts of famines to be found in the chronicles and histories of the period. Our knowledge of famines 'remains somewhat doubtful', Georges Duby remarked in *Rural Economy and Country Life in the Medieval West*, 'for what value can we put on the accounts of chroniclers, who were by nature given to romance and to magnifying dramatic events, the echoes of which had already reached them in a distorted form?'. 'It was just because they were strange and unusual', commented the agrarian historian Slicher van Bath in similar vein, 'that they were recorded in the chronicles.' No doubt the chronicles, like the oral sources on famine just referred to, present many problems of interpretation. Quite apart from any literary embellishments and stylistic effects the chroniclers may have added to their accounts, it is often difficult to tell whether a particular drought or dearth was widespread or merely confined to a small locality: many famines may have entered the written record only because they occurred close to a royal court or to the scribes of a nearby monastery. Without modern census data at their command, medieval chroniclers and their informants could do little more than guess at the extent of the mortality caused to the famine-struck. But the fact that the medieval chronicles 'groan' with reports of famine suggests either that it was indeed a widespread and frequent phenomenon and that life for many people in medieval Europe was singularly precarious, or that the gloomy introspection of the age and the pessimism regarding man's miserable position relative to god and nature found apt expression in the idea of a harsh and tormenting environment and a stern divinity quick to punish the sins of the ungrateful and the ungodly. However, if the well-documented famines elsewhere in the world in the nineteenth and early twentieth centuries are any guide (and they may not be), the often grisly accounts of the medieval chroniclers do not seem excessively doom-laden or fanciful.

If we can understand why famines were so long and so vividly remembered, why they occupied so prominent and enduring a place in the collective consciousness, we can perhaps come closer to an understanding of what famine meant to those who witnessed and experienced it and what, in their minds, distinguished famine from other forms of hunger and suffering. One obvious reason was that, like many other 'natural disasters', they were interpreted as signs and portents, having a significance far beyond the phenomenon itself. Just as for some Nigerian Muslims the drought of 1973 signified 'the wrath of Allah against mankind', so for Christians in late Elizabethan England the famine of the 1590s showed that God was angry with the people. In the words of one contemporary it meant that 'the hand of God is heavy upon us' for 'all windes and ill weather procede directly from the justice of God'. Mankind ignored such divine warnings at its peril, though the precise nature of the offence for which such drastic punishment was being meted out was always a matter open to conjecture. The wickedness of men, the transgressions of rulers, the evil-doing of sorcerers or some scapegoat minority (like the hapless Jews and lepers of fourteenth-century Languedoc), were favoured explanations. But, whatever the precise cause, there was no doubting the divine provenance of famine and the need for human contrition. Rarely, except perhaps where conquest and extortion was seen to be directly involved, were famines held to be the consequence of human greed and artifice alone. Even a monarch's indifference to his subjects' needs and suffering could be interpreted as the execution of a punishment divinely ordained. The involvement of the elements – the failure of the rains, the unseasonal frosts and floods – seemed to place causation beyond human reach and to provide sober confirmation of man's subordination to god and nature. Famine fed apocalyptic visions; and not until man presumed a mastery over nature and took a more selective view of the forms and purposes of godly intervention did famine begin to forfeit its divine associations in the minds of men.

It was important, too, that famines were collective catastrophes. Although few famines were absolute in the sense of arising from a total failure of food supplies or the uniform destitution of all classes of society, they none the less scythed with a broad blade. The magnitude of the calamity dwarfed individual misfortune. Famines were events that touched the lives of millions deeply and directly – one of the reasons why famines lived on in the collective memory so long after the episode itself had passed.

For peasants, labourers and pastoralists, whose existence was always precarious, and who were constantly aware that a bad harvest or two or a sudden flood would be enough to reduce them to starvation level, it was of pressing relevance to keep alive an awareness of past hunger. By Goubert's calculation, every peasant in seventeenth-century France experienced a major subsistence crisis at least once during his or her lifetime. It was thus historically and psychologically significant that famines were recurrent and not (in most societies) once-and-for-all or long-forgotten events. It was the terror of their possible, even probable, return that kept them alive in myth and memory, made cultivators anxiously scan the heavens before planting or harvesting or sleep uneasily when the air was rife with rumours of impending war or drought. There might be a practical value in putting knowledge drawn from the past to service in the present. At the first clear signs of incipient drought and hunger, the father of Wang Lung, the hero of *The Good Earth*, Pearl S. Buck's novel of peasant China, recalls an earlier famine when people were reduced to eating human flesh to stay alive. Ever more practical, Wang Lung's wife urges that they should keep the cores of their harvested maize: 'do not waste them in burning', she says. 'I remember when I was a child in Shantung when years like this came, even the cobs we ground and ate. It is better than grass.'

It is only in the past century or two that western society has shaken off this recurrent dread, and, feeling itself immune to famine, has discarded such cumulative folk experience as redundant. Our lack of awareness of famine as a possible force in our own lives is one of the things that most critically divides us off from our own past and from the lives of a large part of today's Third World population.

In their quest for objectivity and reason, or perhaps from an inability to squeeze the tragedy and horror of famine into academically acceptable form, many writers skirt around the grimmest aspects of famine. William A. Dando in his *Geography of Famine* remarks with apparent regret that famine 'as a descriptive term ... carries emotional overtones'. How could it not! And is the gravity of famine revealed any more effectively by stripping it bare of its emotional burden? Rather too often, possibly recoiling from what they personally find difficult to comprehend or explain, scholars have tried to reduce famine to an exercise in demographic arithmetic or economic logistics, thus imposing their own sense of order and meaning upon the horrific confusion and uncertainty of the famine situation. Statistics have their place; but used alone they obscure as much as they reveal of this ordeal. There comes a point at which the sheer size of famine mortality defies comprehension. Is it possible to understand any difference between a famine in which three million people died and one in which six or seven million perished?

Historically speaking, the bewilderment and terror caused by famine must be counted among its defining characteristics. Something of this experience can occasionally be gleaned from the recollections, songs and tales of those who passed through the famine ordeal themselves, and some recent studies of famine have been especially effective as a result of their incorporation of materials of this kind. More frequently, however, their experiences can only be seen refracted in the accounts of outside observers. The following passage forms part of a letter written by N. M. Cummins, a Justice of the Peace and small landholder in Cork, to the Duke of Wellington in December 1846 as the Irish potato famine was nearing its worst. It provides some illustration of the nature of the 'Great Hunger' and it also shows how deep and disturbing could be the impressions famine made even on those who, though not among its 'victims', observed their agonies at first hand:

Being aware that I should have to witness a scene of frightful hunger, I provided myself with as much bread as five men could carry, and on reaching the spot I was surprised to find the wretched hamlet deserted. I entered some of the hovels to ascertain the cause and the scenes that presented themselves were such as no tongue or pen can convey the slightest idea of. In the first, six famished and ghastly skeletons, to all appearance dead, were huddled in a corner on some filthy straw, their sole covering what seemed a ragged horse-cloth and their wretched legs hanging about, naked above the knees. I approached in horror, and found by a low moaning that they were alive, they were in fever - four children, a woman, and what had once been a man. It is impossible to go through the details, suffice to say, that in a few minutes I was surrounded by at least 200 such phantoms, such frightful spectres as no words can describe. By far the greatest number were delirious either from hunger or from fever. Their demonaic yells are still ringing in my ears, and their horrible images are fixed upon my brain . . . the same morning the police opened a house on the adjoining lands, which was observed shut for many days, and two frozen corpses were found lying upon the mud floor *half devoured by the rats*. A mother, herself in fever, was seen the same day to drag out the corpse of her child, a girl about twelve perfectly naked; and leave it half covered with stones. In another house . . . the dispensary doctor found seven wretches lying, unable to move, under the same cloak - one had been dead for many hours but the others were unable to move either themselves or the corpse.[2]

In the following description, two Western observers reported on the Honan famine in China in 1942 in which an estimated two to three million people died and as many more abandoned their homes in search of food:

The smaller villages were even worse than the market towns. The silence was frightening. People fled the impersonal cruelty of hunger as if a barbarian army were upon them. The villages echoed with emptiness; streets were deserted, . . . doors and windows boarded up
. . .

There were corpses on the road. A girl no more than seventeen, slim and pretty, lay on the damp earth, her lips blue with death; her eyes were open, and rain fell on them. People chipped at bark, pounded it by the roadside for food; vendors sold leaves at a dollar a bundle. A dog digging at a mound was exposing a human body. Ghostlike men were skimming the stagnant pools to eat the green slime of the waters . . .

When a group of mother, baby and two older children became tired from the long hunt for food, the mother, sitting down to nurse the infant, sent the older children on to look for food in the next village; when they returned, the baby was still sucking at the breast of the dead mother. In a fit of frenzy the parents of two children murdered them rather than hear them beg for something to eat. Some families sold all they had for one last big meal, then committed suicide.[3]

Although, as indicated earlier, medieval chronicles have often been suspected of gross exaggeration, they too convey something of the

2. R. Dudley Edwards and T. Desmond Williams, (eds) *The Great Famine*, p. 275.
3. Theodore H. White and Annalee Jacoby, *Thunder out of China*, pp. 166-78.

grimmer aspects of famine, and the fear of famine, through their blunt prose. In the English famine year of 1315 one chronicler recorded that:

> Horse flesh was counted great delicates; the poore stole fatte dogges to eate: some (as it was saide) compelled through famine, in hidde places, did eate the flesh of their owne children, and some stole others which they devoured. Theeves that were in prisons did plucke in pieces those that were newlie brought amongst them and greedily devoured them half alive.[4]

The horror of famine was compounded of many things – having to subsist by scavenging and begging, being reduced to eating 'unclean things', being abandoned by family and friends, dying alone, away from home and uncomforted, being devoured unburied by vultures and wolves. The conventions, the constraints, the securities of everyday life one by one dropped away or were brutally inverted. Men behaved like animals: dogs gnawed at human corpses. The ultimate descent, difficult though it is for us to comprehend it or perhaps even read about without incredulity, was to cannibalism. 'Now', reported the Catholic Bishop of Shansi during the North China famine in 1877, 'they kill the living to have them for food. Husbands eat wives. Parents eat their sons and daughters, and children eat their parents.' Cannibalism was reported more recently, too, as in the bitterly divisive Russian famine of 1932–34. Even where such accounts may legitimately be suspected of exaggeration, and are dismissed as being (as most reports of cannibalism undoubtedly are) second-hand and hearsay, they testify nonetheless to the stark horror famine conveyed to the minds of contemporaries and to succeeding generations. Clearly famine was not just about having enough food to eat or about calorific minima. It was a multiple crisis of subsistence, survival and order. The more protracted and intense the crisis the more the normal order of things collapsed and gave way to all that was abnormal and horrific.

Famine as demographic crisis

One of the ways in which famines impressed themselves upon the collective memory and experience was through the colossal and devastating mortality involved. Famines were above all else 'crises of

---

4. W. Cunningham, *The Growth of English Industry and Commerce during the Early and Middle Ages*, vol. I, p. 388.

mortality', their scale and impact crudely registered in the number of deaths caused.

Famine spelled death on a massive scale, but it is seldom easy to say how many died. Dando in his *Geography of Famine* gives figures of 2 million deaths world-wide for the seventeenth century, 10 million for the eighteenth and 25 million for the nineteenth. In the present century, he suggests, the toll may rise even higher than in the last. Such figures are questionable enough in themselves: to what extent does the apparent increase over the past four centuries merely reflect a more accurate reporting and a more scrupulous recording of famine mortality? But even the totals given seem to fall far short of the likely tally. Some estimates put mortality in the Bengal famine of 1769-70 alone at 10 million, while double that number of lives may have been lost as a result of famine in India in the second half of the nineteenth century. Although India was free of major famines from 1908 to 1942, the Bengal famine of 1943-44 claimed a further 3 million lives. In China an estimated 9 to 13 million people perished in the famine of 1876-79, followed by a further half million in 1920-21 and possibly 2 to 3 million in Honan province in 1943. It is not yet clear how many people died as a result of the famine in China in 1958-61. One estimate puts the figure at 30 million 'excess deaths' (i.e. above the level that would have been expected in 'normal' conditions). Another, more cautiously, suggests at least 23 million, while the Chinese authorities themselves have recently admitted to 16 million deaths from starvation. If these horrific totals even begin to approximate to the truth, then the 1958-61 famine must rank as the largest in human history. Russia, like China and India, often branded in the past a 'land of famine', suffered a loss of some 650,000 lives during a famine in 1891-92, between 1 and 3 million in 1921, and possibly as many as 5 million in 1932-34 (though estimates range widely from 1 to 10 million).

The China famine of the late 1950s apart, international relief operations and medical intervention have significantly reduced the scale of famine mortality in recent years. Nevertheless, in the Bangladesh food crisis of 1974 several hundred thousand people are thought to have died: one writer cites a figure of more than a million 'excess deaths'. And, despite the international attention it aroused, albeit belatedly, the Ethiopian famine of 1984-85 has been held responsible for the death of a million people.

Huge as these numbers are, the extent of famine's demographic impact is perhaps more adequately conveyed through the percentage of the population who perished. In the Bengal famine of 1769-70 the lives of about a third of the inhabitants of this populous province are said to have been lost. Roughly the same percentage of the population died in the famine in three districts of Orissa in eastern India in 1866, and a similar proportion perished in the Ethiopian famine of 1888-92. In the drought-prone *sertão*, or wilderness, of northeastern Brazil, about a third of the population died in the famine of 1825; but in the even more severe crisis of 1877-78 about half of the one million inhabitants of the state of Ceará were lost through deaths from starvation and disease. In the North China famine of 1876-79 the loss was in excess of a third, and in the worst-hit provinces of Shansi and Shantung it may well have been more than fifty per cent. Ireland's 'Great Hunger' was instrumental in reducing the population by about a fifth, from the 8.2 million recorded in the 1841 census to 6.6 a decade later. However, more than half of this decline was due to emigration: approximately 800,000 deaths were caused by starvation and by famine-related diseases.

Within a particular province or district famine mortality might range far higher than even these figures suggest. After severe famines, like those in southern India and North China in the late 1870s, hundreds of villages stood empty and deserted, houses were unoccupied, and arable land was not taken up for cultivation again for many years. Sometimes it took several decades for the population to return to pre-famine levels. A famine in northern India in the territory around Delhi in 1783-84 was said to have 'unpeopled 600 villages . . . , 200 of which still stood empty in 1820'. Shansi, which bore the brunt of the North China famine of 1876-79, contained fewer inhabitants in 1953 than it had before the famine began, despite the rapid growth of population in China as a whole. These figures speak only of those who died. They say nothing of the millions whose lives were wrecked by famine but who somehow survived. Although relatively few people actually died of hunger in northern China between 1928 and 1931, an estimated 57 million were affected by famine, 12 million of them severely. The extent of their suffering and deprivation is not easily calculated. Some survived the famine itself, only to succumb later to disease and the debilitating effects of persistent undernourishment.

Mortality statistics can give only a rough impression and it would be unrealistic to credit them with any mathematical precision. Until the last century or two few governments kept reliable and detailed records of vital data. Historians who have tried to reconstruct the famine mortality of the remoter past have had to try to compensate for this deficiency by using parish records, tax returns and similar sources, but these seldom provide a dependable picture of mortality trends over a wider area. Many famines occurred in regions remote from central governments' surveillance, or happened in times of war and political upheaval when the administration was in disarray or preoccupied with other, more politically pressing, tasks. Even where some form of birth and death registration existed, famine mortality was often grossly under-reported. Local officials themselves fell ill, died, or deserted their posts; the deaths of villagers who wandered off in search of food elsewhere passed unrecorded.

Although discussion of famine's demographic impact has concentrated on assessments of mortality, two other features call for comment. One was a sharp decline in the birth-rate. There were many reasons for this. Hunger diminished sexual appetite; marriages were postponed or cancelled through the death of the prospective partners; families were broken up through migration and death, or could not afford the extra burden of more mouths to feed. Thus there was a fall in the number of conceptions. Due to malnutrition and stress, women became temporarily infertile (a condition known technically as famine amenorrhea); abortion and infanticide prevented dwindling resources from being stretched still further or spared an unborn or new-born child inevitable suffering. The fall in the birth-rate was, however, likely to be one of the more short-term effects of famine. Once the crisis was over families often responded with more births to replace the children who had died and as insurance against future losses. A second important demographic feature was migration. Much famine migration was short-term and over relatively short distances, and once conditions improved, survivors returned to their homes and farms. In Ireland's 'Great Hunger' and in the North China famine of 1876–79 as many people migrated as died. But in both these cases many migrants did not return but found permanent homes in another province or another land. In this way migration, like mortality, has been one of the more enduring demographic consequences of famine.

Assessment of famine mortality is further complicated by the disease factor. In most famines the mortality from epidemic disease has greatly exceeded that from actual starvation deaths. In the Irish potato famine the 20,000 deaths directly attributed to starvation were outnumbered by the 193,000 from 'fever' (an unhelpfully vague description), 125,000 from dysentery and diarrhoea, and 22,000 from dropsy. Similarly, during the course of the Bengal famine of 1943–44 starvation was identified as the cause of death in only about five per cent of cases: cholera, malaria, and smallpox accounted for the great majority of the three million deaths. (However, by the 1940s, and even during the nineteenth century, the colonial administration in India was loath to acknowledge starvation as a cause of death in more than a tiny minority of cases: famine mortality has long been too political a matter to escape official editing and censorship). It was, therefore, mainly through disease, and especially epidemic disease, that famine had its greatest demographic impact. But the exact nature of the relationship between hunger, malnutrition and epidemic mortality remains unclear. Some epidemics obviously occur (and cause heavy mortality) among populations without famine being in attendance. In some instances, epidemics precede famines and may even help to precipitate them, for a population immobilized by disease may be unable to plant and harvest its crops, hunt, fish, or tend its animals. Plant and animal diseases have a place, too, in occasioning or intensifying famine conditions. The blight that ruined Ireland's potatoes and reduced them to a rotten and inedible pulp was the proximate cause of famine in 1846–47. The cattle epidemic known as rinderpest, which swept through eastern and southern Africa in the 1890s, caused the destruction of the herds that were the primary source of livelihood for African pastoralist communities. They were left without subsistence and the means of exchange to obtain other foodstuffs.

But with singular frequency epidemics have pressed close on the heels of hunger, doubling, sometimes trebling, the usual rates of mortality. Goubert reckoned that during subsistence crises in seventeenth-century France, mortality sometimes rose to four or five times the 'normal' level. He claimed that epidemic disease was a major cause of this soaring mortality.

The reasons for the intertwining of epidemics and famines appear to be both physiological and social. Malnutrition weakens the body's immune responses. There is a diminished resistance to infection and a reduced capacity to recover from it afterwards. The young and the old, already the most vulnerable members of the community, are especially susceptible to epidemic attack. Pregnant and lactating women are at risk because of the high nutritional demands made on their bodies. As Amartya Sen has shown for the Bengal famine of 1943–44, the pattern of mortality in terms of age and sex continued to be much as before but at levels greatly inflated by the general debility of the population due to hunger and malnutrition. Other factors, however, also come into play. As already mentioned, one of the primary responses to famine was migration. This self-mobilization of the weak and hungry had a multiplying effect, spreading disease to regions and to social groups not directly affected by hunger. The wanderers and migrants, as during the Irish famine, huddled together for warmth at night, or congregated at relief camps, in work-houses and hospitals, in towns and ports, anywhere where food and charity might be found. But, in crowding together in such confined and insanitary places, the famine-struck provided almost ideal conditions for the transmission of epidemic diseases or for the fleas and lice that were their secret vectors. Rags and clothes sold to buy food or stripped from corpses further aided disease dissemination. So did the practice in India of disposing of uncremated and unburied corpses in rivers and wells. Personal hygiene was forgotten; people neglected to wash or drank filthy and contaminated water. Care and quarantining of the sick ceased at the very time when the public health services (already inadequate in Ireland before the potato famine) were being over-whelmed by the number of cases urgently needing attention. Consuming 'famine foods' - unripe grain, bark, grass, roots, even earth - in a desperate attempt to assuage hunger, caused intestinal irritation, diarrhoea and vomiting, and resulted in further weakening of the body. The high level of famine mortality, in other words, was partly a consequence of the nature of the very expedients people adopted to try to escape from hunger and of the disruption famine caused to customary patterns of social behaviour.

The prominence of cholera as a cause of sickness and death in the famines of the nineteenth and twentieth century is a reminder that the disease factor was far from being historically constant. In 1817 cholera erupted, possibly for the first time (at least in recent times), as a major epidemic disease. From its home in the murky reservoirs and rain-swollen rivers of Bengal it spread rapidly to other parts of southern Asia and then raced on, further afield, to Southeast Asia and China, to Russia and western Europe, to Africa and the Americas. Although many cholera epidemics (like those that reached England in the 1830s, 1840s and 1860s) were not specifically famine-related, they preyed heavily upon the poor and undernourished living in insanitary conditions in the capital cities and industrial slums. But in many parts of the world cholera and famine had a lethal connection. In India repeatedly throughout the nineteenth century epidemics of cholera multiplied famine mortality two- or three-fold; in the Russian famine of 1891-92 nearly half of the 650,000 deaths reported were attributed to cholera; and in China, in eastern Africa and in Ireland (in the later stages of the 'Great Hunger'), cholera swelled the famine toll. The cholera vibrio seemed to flourish most vigorously where human misery was greatest.

Smallpox, too, acquired a deadly association with famine - again particularly in India, where smallpox remained endemic until the 1970s, but also in Brazil where a large part of the mortality in the 1876–77 famine was caused by smallpox. The global dissemination of these diseases – smallpox was unknown in the Americas before it was unwittingly introduced by the Spanish conquistadores in the early sixteenth century, just as cholera did not leave its Indian homeland until the early nineteenth – suggests one possible explanation for the extraordinary scale of famine mortality in recent centuries, and only comparatively recently has medical intervention done much to counter the famine-fed ravages of these epidemic diseases. But perhaps famine has always found an ally in disease of one kind or another. Long before cholera was known to the West, typhus was all too familiar as 'famine fever', and though controversy surrounds the relationship between famine and bubonic plague in the fourteenth century, it is certainly possible that the Black Death spread so rapidly and with such fatal consequences in western Europe because much of the population was already ill-fed. Plague, according to Le Roy Ladurie, was the 'holocaust of the undernourished', the Malthusian day of reckoning for a hungry and over-populated Europe.

Whatever the precise nature of the undoubtedly complex relationship between famines and epidemics, it is clear that famines have had a profound demographic and social impact not just through the number of deaths and the amount of suffering directly attributable to them, but also through the diseases that accompanied them and formed part of the wider 'famine syndrome'. Although epidemic diseases, unlike hunger deaths, might affect people of all classes, the evidence suggests that mortality was generally greatest among the poor and landless, thus giving epidemiological emphasis to existing social divisions and possibly, too, to the political tensions and conflicts arising from them. Conversely, however, the physical incapacity brought about by disease as well as hunger may have made it all the more difficult for the famine-struck to protest effectively against those whom they saw as manipulating the grain markets for their personal profit or who, for all their own wealth and power, remained indifferent to the suffering of the poor.

Famine in the pre-modern or pre-industrial age, as the French historians have shown, was not an isolated event but formed part of a pattern of recurrent demographic and subsistence crises which cumulatively kept mortality at a high level. The plea for deliverance from '*peste, fame et bello*' was an accurate reflection of the insecurities of what has aptly been called the 'biological *ancien régime*'. Periodic catastrophes of this kind formed part of the recurrent rhythms of the pre-industrial age; and it was not until the eighteenth and nineteenth centuries that western and northern Europe began to liberate themselves from the cyclical tyranny of hunger and enter an age of low, stable mortality. In ridding itself of famine Europe almost certainly reduced its susceptibility to many epidemic diseases as well. A population that was more regularly and more amply fed was better equipped to resist the ravages of plague, typhus and cholera as well.

Famine chronology

The relationship with epidemic disease highlights another aspect of famines – their duration. Through a series of long- and short-term expedients (discussed in a later chapter), rural societies could generally survive the effects of one bad harvest. Some peasants produced two, in some places even three, crops a year, and one good harvest (aided by stocks carried over from one year to the next as an insurance against dearth) might go a long way towards compensating for an earlier shortfall. But famine often operated as a cumulative process, through a crippling succession of disasters rather than a single blow. One bad harvest followed another, flood succeeded a year without rain (as happened so disastrously in the Orissa famine of 1866) or, as has not infrequently occurred in Africa, months of drought and hunger were followed by a plague of devouring locusts, making recovery without external aid almost impossible. In England between 1460 and 1759 the record of grain prices indicates that there were deficient harvests on average once every four years, but the effect of the bad harvests was aggravated by the fact that they often came bunched together. A cheering run of four good harvests was followed by a devastating sequence of three poor ones, some bad enough to trigger a famine. In Ireland, the potato blight spoilt only part of the harvest of 1845, but any prospect of recovery was crushed by the almost total failure of the crop in 1846 and 1847. By that date the peasants had consumed their seed potatoes, exhausted their slender assets, and become demoralized by their plight.

Famine has its own internal chronology. As hunger seldom kills outright and immediately – one reason why epidemic disease is so frequently the proximate cause – the symptoms of growing hunger may not be apparent to outsiders until destitution and debilitation have already reached an advanced stage. The onset of mass-hunger has often long preceded its official recognition. Equally, the mortality attributable to famine-related epidemics is likely to continue for months, even years, after the main subsistence crisis has passed. The Bengal famine, identified by British officials with a single year, 1943, and resulting (in the opinion of the official Famine Commission set up to investigate it) in about 1.5 million deaths, is now seen as extending over at least two years and lasting on through the effects of epidemic disease into 1944 or even 1945–46 at a cost of more than 3 million lives. Amartya Sen has suggested that the famine in fact fell into three phases: the first from the beginning of 1942 to March 1943 when the symptoms of an impending economic crisis began to manifest themselves; a second phase, characterized by high food prices and a peak of starvation deaths, running from March 1943 to November 1943; and a third phase, lasting for most of 1944 and marked by high levels of 'famine-induced' epidemic mortality. Such an approach has the virtue of recognizing the full extent of famine's impact, spread over several years and not confined to a crisis of acute hunger alone. But it also raises questions as to when a famine can finally be said to have ceased and normality been restored.

The duration of famine can be reckoned according to a variety of different criteria. The definition made by those actually subject to the famine might vary greatly from the official definitions. The former might start with the first warning signs of approaching calamity, such as the delayed arrival of the rains and the first withering of the standing crops. The latter might begin only when food prices climbed to abnormal heights or when the by-now-inescapable signs of distress among the starving poor were afforded official recognition. In the Bengal famine of 1943, for instance, official ignorance and indifference were only breached when tens of thousands of destitutes started flooding into Calcutta from the famine-stricken districts and city newspapers began to publish harrowing reports, supported by photographs, of the famine's effects. Equally, the officials' definition might end with the closure of state-managed relief works, though this might happen many months before the famine survivors felt themselves free of its coils. The rise and fall of grain prices, the hyperbolic surge and slump of epidemic mortality, the statistics of migration and of crime, the numbers on relief works or dependent upon state charity – all these suggest alternative, if broadly overlapping, criteria of what constituted famine and what marked its onset, duration, and conclusion.

The Irish potato famine offers a striking example of conflicting definitions. Most historians date the beginning of the famine from the mass starvation that began in 1846 and see it as continuing through to the census of 1851 and the first clear signs of agricultural recovery. But Cecil Woodham-Smith in her popular account of *The Great*

Hunger begins with the arrival of the blight in 1845 and closes prematurely in 1849 when the full demographic effects and political consequences of the famine were still far from over. Edwards and Williams, by contrast, in their edited history see the famine through from 1845 to the final closure of relief works in 1852. A famine is evidently an 'event' capable of many definitions.

2

Theories of Famine Causation

In the past 'acts of God' and 'freaks of nature' were seen as self-sufficient explanations for why men hungered and died. In cataloguing the reasons why famines occurred, Cornelius Walford a century ago drew a ready distinction between what he called 'natural causes', like drought, flood, late frosts and exceptional snowfalls, and 'man-made causes', such as warfare, blockades and the deliberate hoarding of grain. We are now more sceptical about blaming God or crediting nature and, although we continue to refer to a particular drought, flood or war as causing a famine, we are more disposed to see these as only precipitating or contributory factors, inadequate in themselves to account for famine's far-reaching disaster or to explain why one society is crippled by drought while another remains singularly unaffected. Increasingly famine is regarded as a complex phenomenon, in which climate is only one factor. Famine has come to be seen more as a symptom than cause, a sign of a society's inner weaknesses and not just a consequence of temporary climatic aberrations.

Climate

It would appear that some areas of the world, by virtue of their location and the vagaries of climate they suffer, are particularly famine-prone. Earthquakes, cyclones, droughts, and floods occur more frequently in one region than another. In some semi-arid areas the ecological balance between man and environment seems intrinsically precarious, and the crops that are able to flourish in favourable years of high rainfall wither in the intervening period when precipitation is scant. Nor is climate itself necessarily a constant factor. Long-term shifts as well as short-term variations in temperature and rainfall have ruined crops, dried up pasturage and gradually undermined a society's apparently secure subsistence base. The extension of European agriculture to Iceland and Greenland in the early Middle Ages and the exploration and settlement of the Vikings as far away as the 'Vinland' coast of North America were developments made possible by a period of relatively mild climatic conditions between the eighth and twelfth centuries. But these advances were halted and then reversed by the onset of stormy, wet weather, the southward drift of the Arctic pack-ice into North Atlantic waters, and a general lowering of temperatures in northern Europe in the thirteenth and fourteenth centuries. The widespread famine of 1315–16 in England, France and other parts of northwestern Europe has been attributed to a succession of cold, wet summers that hampered agricultural operations, prevented corn from ripening, and signalled a change from earlier, more favourable, climatic conditions. The 'Little Ice Age' of the sixteenth and seventeenth centuries (which allowed fairs to be held on a frozen River Thames) seems to have had a similarly negative effect, depressing agricultural productivity, spoiling harvests, and (in the 1520s and 1590s in particular) causing widespread food shortages.

Even in more recent times short-term climatic changes have had a dramatic effect upon food production. The eruption of the Indonesian volcano of Tomboro in April 1815 threw millions of tons of dust and debris into the atmosphere, shutting out the sunlight, blighting summers, and causing bitterly cold winters as far away as western Europe and North America. According to John D. Post, this natural, if exceptional, phenomenon was responsible for the western world's 'last great subsistence crisis' in 1816–19, plunging many European countries into hunger and distress, and triggering social and political unrest. Several times, too, during the course of the nineteenth century – notably in 1833–36, 1866–68 and 1876–79 – the climatic variability associated with the northerly and southerly oscillations of the Intertropical Convergence Zone brought drought or unseasonal rainfall to northeastern Brazil, western and northern Africa, India, China and Japan. The late 1870s in particular witnessed the century's severest droughts and famines in Brazil, India and China.

That famine could result over such vast areas of the globe (despite the many economic, social and political differences between the countries affected) from shared climatic conditions, would seem a powerful argument in favour of some form of climatic determinism. The history of famine in India, too, seems to substantiate the importance, if not the primacy, of climate. Every major famine of the nineteenth century was preceded by the partial, sometimes complete, failure of the monsoon rains on which Indian agriculture has traditionally been so heavily dependent. Even today, despite the Green Revolution and the extensive use of tube-wells, the abundance and timeliness of these life-giving rains is still (as the drought of

1987–88 reminds us) vital to the subsistence of many millions of people.

Whether in discussing the famines of the more distant past or the recent famines in the Sahel and Ethiopia, geographers have given prominence to the role of climate even when they have shied away from advancing it as the solitary cause. Historians, however, have been more wary. In part they have been reacting against the more extravagant claims made in the past by geographers like the American Ellsworth Huntington. Writing in the early decades of this century, Huntington confidently declared climatic change to be 'one of the controlling causes of the rise and fall of the great nations of the world' and maintained that the civilizations of antiquity had 'risen or fallen in harmony with favourable or unfavourable conditions of climate'. According to Huntington's once-popular thesis, civilizations flourished only in certain favourable climatic conditions (which just happened closely to resemble those of western Europe and the northern United States in his day), and any departure from these, such as a long-term shift in temperature or rainfall, was sufficient to spark social unrest, prompt wholesale emigration, cause famine, and ultimately bring about the collapse of an entire civilization. Historians have found such sweeping climatic theories almost impossible to digest, despite a growing appreciation of the importance of climate as one among many factors influencing economic and social change. 'Underlying all such theories', commented Le Roy Ladurie, 'is the lazy but highly contestable postulate that climate exercises a determining influence on history'.

Other considerations may also have swayed historians away from affording climate too great a prominence – an unwillingness, perhaps, to accept that anything so momentous as human history can be shaped by anything so commonplace as weather, or a predeliction for Malthusian explanations grounded in excessive population growth and constricted agricultural productivity. Climate is allowed an instrumental not a causative role. Hence the underlying reason why western Europe went hungry in 1314–15, according to the Malthusian argument, was because it was over-populated relative to the scale of its food production and the level of agrarian technology and economic organization at the time. Europe's peasant farmers were unable to cope with the problems posed by a succession of wet summers and deficient harvests. Climatic variations are seen as too short-term, too peripheral to provoke a major crisis of subsistence like that which overtook early fourteenth-century Europe. By the same token, once much of Europe (by the end of the eighteenth century or the early nineteenth) had developed agricultural techniques and evolved social and economic institutions capable of lessening the impact of occasional bad harvests and unseasonal or inclement weather, it no longer had famine to fear.

While happily accepting the broad argument, I have reservations about downgrading the climatic factor too much. Precisely because today we can feel confident of our capacity to tame or to defy the elements, we are in danger of underestimating their importance to the agriculture of a less versatile age and to a society whose technology and economic resources were less developed than today's. We may treat the weather with relative indifference (unless we follow cricket or grow outdoor tomatoes), knowing that our future subsistence and survival are not tied to its vagaries. But we should not therefore lose sight of its direct, often overwhelming, consequences for pre- or non-industrial societies. Nor should we overlook the psychological and social effects of drought and flood in many parts of the Third World even today – the gnawing fear of famine that they quickly arouse, a fear that can be sufficient in itself to send alarm surging through the market-places, spark hoarding and food riots, and cause grain prices to soar. In so confidently demoting climate and all that stems from it to a secondary and merely instrumental role we risk being too casual and detached about its importance to societies distant in time or space from our own.

To reason thus is not to argue for the restitution of a kind of Huntingtonian determinism, but rather to allow climate its due as historically a powerful influence over the lives of the mass of the population and a continuing source of apprehension and insecurity in their collective experience and consciousness. But, at the same time, it is evident that climate alone does not explain why and when famines occur, why drought or flood can pitch one society headlong into famine while leaving another virtually unscathed. As Dando points out, while drought has sometimes been a factor in causing famines in Russia, there have been many times of dearth and hunger when it has *not* been a significant influence. There have been droughts in India since the First World War without famine automatically following in their wake. Arguably, too, the more nearly one approaches to the present day, the more even non-industrial societies have been subject to factors other than climate (such as the negative consequences of international trade) which have increased their vulnerability to 'natural disasters' (and hence to famine), or which have made once effective forms of adaptation to climatic variation and periodic food shortages infinitely more difficult to maintain. Clearly, something more than climate must be involved.

This has been the view of many informed writers on the recent droughts and famines in Africa. In their opinion lack of rainfall or other such 'natural disasters' fail to explain the underlying causes of recurrent distress. Indeed, as Nicole Ball has argued, concentrating upon such phenomena may lead to a neglect of more fundamental reasons for mass hunger:

> A drought, like all other 'natural' disasters, should properly be viewed as resulting from a combination of social, political, economic, and environmental factors. The interaction of these elements, over the long-term, can seriously reduce the ability of a system to cope with new and/or suddenly intensified stresses. This interaction creates the 'conditions for disaster' and makes a breakdown at some point inevitable. Because it is often a natural phenomenon - too little rainfall, in the case of drought - which produces the unacceptable stress on the system, the resultant breakdown tends to be characterized as a 'natural' disaster. This definition allows analysts to overlook the more fundamental problems which generate or exacerbate ecological instability.[1]

Instead, therefore, of seeing climate as a self-sufficient explanation for famine, such writers look instead to a long-term deterioration of Africans' control over their own economic and social systems. Through the inroads of colonialism and an international market economy dominated by Western capitalism, Africans have seemingly lost the capacity to control their productive forces and to manage the environment in accordance with their own needs and past experience. A drought is thus an event which brings these deep-seated and structural problems to a head.

There may, of course, be dangers in reading the complexities of famine in Africa today into the famines of other times, other places, and other peoples. Perhaps, in some respects, the famines of an earlier age were less complicated affairs. Without the pressures of international capitalism to distort local economies, without railways and planes to speed the importation of foodstuffs into drought-hit areas, and without international aid and medical relief operations to lessen famine's impact, climate had a more immediate and brutal impact. When the rains failed, when floods swept away crops and houses, people starved for simple want of food.

1. Nicole Ball, 'Understanding the Causes of African Famine', *Journal of Modern African Studies*, 1976, p. 520.

The rejection of short-term explanations for the causes of famine in contemporary Africa and the doubts that have been raised in that connection about climatic determinism underline the importance of an historical approach to famine, an approach which is able to encompass climatic and other environmental factors, but which also takes into account changes in social relations within a community and the economic and political structures that bind it to a wider world. Also, unless we close our eyes to the frequency of subsistence crises and outright famine in Europe before the mid-nineteenth century and claim that famine in Third World countries today is a product of their peculiarly unstable climates, we need to understand why in the past century or two famine has disappeared from the West but has remained entrenched, perhaps has become even more extensive, in other areas of the world. The answers surely lie elsewhere than in climate alone.

Population

After climate, the most popular explanation for famine has surely been 'over-population'. In claiming a correlation between mass starvation and an 'excessive' population growth that outstrips available food supplies, this theory has the (largely misleading) appeal of apparently explaining famine through a direct and easily-understood causative relationship.

$$\text{Too many mouths} + \text{too little food} = \text{famine}$$

A simple but deadly equation. Of late, the over-population theory has been further elaborated and supported by being coupled with current concern about 'environmental degradation'. Partly, it is argued, as a result of rapid population growth putting unsustainable pressure on the land, but also through reckless commercial exploitation of natural resources, the environment of many parts of the world (and it is generally the Third World that is singled out for comment as if similar processes were not at work elsewhere as well) is undergoing rapid deterioration. Over-worked and eroded soils lose their productive capacity; pastures dry up and become dustbowls through over-grazing; the wholesale destruction of forests and natural vegetation intensifies the effects of flood and drought. In such ways, singly and cumulatively, as the case of Africa in the 1970s and 1980s is seen to demonstrate, man's greed, profligacy and ecological insensitivity have been the root cause of the major famines of recent times.

Whatever the merits or demerits of these theories, it is worth noting that there is little intrinsically new about them. The idea of an overcrowded and worn-out planet has surfaced and resurfaced many times throughout history, especially in times of uncertainty and gloom about the future. Ecological pessimism was a part, for instance, of the early Christian Fathers' view of a 'vitiated' nature, filled with thorns and thistles since man's fall and expulsion from the Garden of Eden. Sixteen centuries before Malthus, Tertullian, the North African Christian writer, world-wearily lamented the great 'density of human beings' on the earth:

> We weigh upon the world; its resources hardly suffice to support us. As our needs grow larger, so do our protests that already nature does not sustain us. In truth, plague, famine, wars and earthquakes must be regarded as a blessing to civilization, since they prune away the luxuriant growth of the human race.

But since it is with Malthus that the 'over-population' theory is most commonly identified (and since his views on famine have profoundly influenced subsequent discussion of the topic), it is as well to begin by looking at his contribution to the debate.

Two considerations seem to have moved T. R. Malthus to write his *Essay on the Principle of Population*, which was first published in 1798, but substantially revised and extended in 1803. One of his aims was to draw public attention to what he saw as the disastrous consequences of the extension of England's Poor Laws through the Speenhamland system. Initiated by a group of Berkshire magistrates in 1795 but quickly applied nationwide, this made provision for poor relief from the rates by subsidizing paupers on a scale related to the current price of bread. It virtually guaranteed them a basic income regardless of whether they worked or not. In Malthus's view this recklessly encouraged the growth of the pauper class and allowed them to bear children free of any personal responsibility for their support. It stimulated population growth without promoting any corresponding expansion in agricultural production, and since, in Malthus's view the food supply was relatively inflexible, food given to the workhouse poor to consume in their idleness was food in effect denied to the more worthy and industrious of England's labouring classes.

Malthus's other reason for writing his *Essay* was as a rebuttal to the free-thinking optimism of contemporary writers like the Marquis de Condorcet in France, with his belief in the indefinite perfectibility of the human spirit, and the Englishman William Godwin, whose

Enquiry concerning Political Justice had appeared in 1793. Where
Godwin passionately believed that social institutions were a source of
misery and injustice and that man would be better off freed from their
constraints, Malthus concluded that, while such institutions might
cause 'much mischief to society', they were 'in reality, light and
superficial in comparison with those deeper-seated causes of evil
which result from the laws of nature and the passions of mankind'.
The optimism of the age and the faith in reason and human nature
which helped to inspire the French Revolution was in his view
rendered groundless by the inherent tendency (already evident from
the example of England's paupers) for population to increase faster
than the means of subsistence. Not sharing the confidence of some of
his contemporaries in an ever-abundant nature, Malthus believed the
food supply to be relatively inelastic, increasing at best by arithmetical
progression, while population rose in geometrical leaps and bounds.
The Malthusian law of population thus posited, Karl Polanyi pointed
out in *The Great Transformation*,

> . . . a relationship between the fertility of man and that of the soil. In
> both cases the forces in play were the forces of Nature, the animal
> instinct of sex and the growth of vegetation in a given soil . . . there was
> a natural limit beyond which human beings could not multiply and that
> limit was set by the available food supply.

The tendency for population to outstrip subsistence was only
constrained, Malthus argued, by the operation of certain 'preventive'
and 'positive' checks. The 'preventive checks', which received fuller
consideration in the later versions of the *Essay*, consisted of the limits
set upon population increase by human foresight and abstinence,
through celibacy and late marriages in particular. Ironically, in view of
the frequency with which his name is now linked with contraception
as a means of population control, Malthus, an Anglican clergyman at
the time he wrote the first version of his *Essay*, did not approve of this
artificial method of limiting the number of births. He was equally
aware that in some parts of the world population was held down by
other methods, such as abortion and infanticide, which he also could
not countenance. Only in the most advanced civilizations, he believed,
was the 'moral restraint' necessary for the voluntary restriction of
population growth to be found. Throughout history and in his own
age, Malthus saw population more commonly and more brutally
constrained by the operation of the 'positive checks' of war, pestilence
and famine. In periodically sweeping away the excess population,

these maintained a rough equilibrium between population and sub-sistence. For Malthus, therefore, famine's significance lay not in any intrinsic character of its own, but in the manner in which it operated alongside other destructive forces to remind man of his continuing subordination to the 'laws of nature and the passions of mankind'.

Since Malthus regarded the 'great law of necessity which prevents population from increasing in any country beyond the food which it can produce or acquire' to be 'so open to our view, so obvious and evident to our understanding, that we cannot for a moment doubt it', he did not see any need to analyse the relationship between popu-lation and subsistence in detail. Instead he offered historical and contemporary illustrations of what he took to be its operation. As several of his critics have been quick to point out, Malthus gave scant consideration to the ways in which available quantities of food might be unequally apportioned – whether through manipulation and control of supplies by the wealthy and powerful or as a result of geographical obstacles or transport difficulties in preventing a more effective distribution. Measuring aggregate food production against population totals was bound to be misleading. Some people might starve while others in the same country, in the same parish even, lived in comfort and dined in plenty.

Nor did Malthus attempt to explain why his 'positive checks' should work in the manner he claimed. Not all epidemics, in practice, have shown such neat discrimination between rich and poor, between 'over-populated' societies and those apparently living easily within their means of subsistence. Even in times of dearth and famine, as pointed out in the previous chapter, the relationship between hunger and epidemic disease is by no means clear-cut. Although many historians (Le Roy Ladurie among them) persist in seeing the Black Death of the fourteenth century as the inevitable purging of an over-populated Europe, straining at the margins of subsistence, others (like John Hatcher) have argued that repeated plague epidemics continued to deplete Europe's population long after any 'excess' had been removed and way below the capacity of agriculture to sustain. Despite rising wage levels and an age of relative prosperity for the cultivators and artisans who survived the holocaust of the Black Death, the population remained at an exceptionally low level due to the continuing ravages of disease. In this instance, at least, there appears, therefore, to be no direct correlation between food availability and population size or between subsistence levels and the devastation caused by epidemic disease. Indeed, Malthus, the country clergyman, deployed his 'positive checks' with an almost apocalyptic venom. War, pestilence,

and famine rush in more like avenging angels, to punish mankind's
immoderation and profligacy, than as the result of any clearly defined
economic or demographic principles.

Malthus's ideas of what constituted subsistence were, besides, constricted by an enduring belief (shared by many of his contemporaries)
that agriculture formed the economy's only truly productive sector
and that agriculture offered little scope for increased output. Looking
back on the precariousness of Europe's demographic *ancien régime*,
seeing pauperism in his own day in contention with prosperity and
apparently threatening to engulf it, Malthus cannot perhaps be blamed
for having failed to appreciate the momentous developments that were
already transforming Britain. As E. A. Wrigley has recently remarked,
'it was Malthus's fate to frame an analysis of the relationship between
population, economy and society during the last generation to which it
was applicable'. Although the Irish famine of the 1840s might seem to
bear out his direst prognostications, in the rest of the British Isles
improved agricultural productivity, better transport, the increasing
importation of foodstuffs financed by the growth of commerce and
industry, and the rapid progress of urbanization exploded the
parameters of Malthus's narrow subsistence equation. Rapid population growth not only failed to trigger Malthusian checks; it also
proved compatible with a general rise in the standard of living. Only
further afield (and this is an issue to which I shall return in the final
chapter), in a famine-struck India and China, could Malthus's theory
be seen to square with nineteenth-century realities. Although it was
not difficult to find ample evidence of 'vice' and 'misery' in Europe,
this could be more readily attributed (as Marx was not alone in
pointing out) to the unequal distribution of wealth, property and
power rather than to any inherent inflexibility or imbalance in the
relationship between population and subsistence, between man and
nature.

In ranking 'positive' above 'preventive' checks as restraining
influences on population growth, Malthus failed to appreciate, too,
the extent to which increasing prosperity and material security,
accompanied by rising expectations and the growing use of contraception, could operate in favour of effective and voluntary birth
control. This has been a striking feature of western and westernizing
societies in the twentieth century. But it is possible that it had
historical precedents, too. Some recent scholars have argued, for
example, that even in the pre-industrial society of Tokugawa Japan
peasant households deliberately held down their numbers (though not
necessarily by methods Malthus would have approved) in order to

maintain their material conditions and to save them from want and loss of status. Although famines certainly occurred (and in the 1780s and 1830s in particular resulted in heavy mortality), late marriages, voluntary celibacy, abortion and female infanticide, possibly did more to restrict population growth than famine alone. If this is indeed the case (and the evidence remains contentious), it further calls in question Malthus's presumptions about the inevitable operation of the 'laws of nature' and gives fresh emphasis to the importance of cultural and social factors (the reasons why one society seeks to restrict population while another does not) in any explanation of demographic trends.

Neo-Malthusianism and its critics

Since the 1950s, stimulated by famines and food crises in the Third World, there has been a strong revival of interest in Malthusian theory. It is, however, a Malthusianism recast to meet the needs and fears of the present age. Population in the Third World is seen to have risen sharply, especially since the Second World War, largely as a result of improved medical services and technology. Rising population levels have, it is claimed (not altogether accurately), outrun food production. With the removal of one 'positive check' in disease, the field for another, in famine, is presumed to be immense; and whether neo-Malthusians have read Malthus or not, they often bring to their writing something of their mentor's own alarm and the apocalyptic vision. 'The battle to feed all of humanity is over', declared Paul Ehrlich in *The Population Bomb* in 1968. 'The famines of the 1970s are upon us – and hundreds of millions of people are going to starve to death before this decade is out.' The reason is presumed to be glaringly obvious, as clearly self-evident as it was to Malthus. 'The stork', as William and Paul Paddock put it so succinctly in their influential and provocative book *Famine - 1975!*, has 'passed the plough'. With too little food to go round and too many mouths to feed, catastrophe is automatically 'foredoomed'. Famine is predicted on a massive, indeed global, scale.

That such emotionally Malthusian arguments continue to be flourished about is surely revealing about the persistence (despite our own relative freedom from want) of a deep and continuing fear of famine and deprivation in the collective psyche of the West. It reflects a sense of insecurity, as real today as in Malthus's age, that the poor will indeed inherit the earth, and, by their profligacy and weight of numbers, rob the 'haves' of their food and reduce them to the penury of the 'have-nots'. Susan George captures the underlying nature of this famine-phobia in urging the West to critically re-examine the motives behind the 'myth' of 'over-population':

> Certainly we are afraid – afraid that increasing numbers in the Third World will one day demand from us their due and lower our own standard of living; fearful that the pressures of population may finally demonstrate that 'the only solution is revolution'.[2]

But, more than in Malthus's day, the fear of the poor is transposed to other cultures and other races. The fear that the Third World will gobble up the First adds to the depth of the underlying anger and alarm that finds expression in at least the wilder expressions of neo-Malthusian logic. Witness, for example, Ehrlich's own observations in the opening pages of *The Population Bomb*:

> I have understood the population explosion intellectually for a long time. I came to understand it emotionally one stinking hot night in Delhi a few years ago. My wife and daughter and I were returning to our hotel in an ancient taxi. The seats were hopping with fleas. The only functional gear was third. As we crawled through the city, we entered a crowded slum area. The temperature was well over 100° F; the air was a haze of dust and smoke. The streets were alive with people. People eating, people washing, people sleeping. People visiting, arguing, and screaming. People thrusting their hands through the taxi window, begging. People defecating and urinating. People clinging to buses. People herding animals. People, people, people, people. As we moved slowly through the mob, hand horn squawking, the dust, noise, heat, and cooking fires gave the scene a hellish aspect. Would we ever get to our hotel? All three of us were, frankly, frightened. It seemed that anything could happen – but, of course, nothing did. . . . since that night I've known the *feel* of over-population.

By making the inhabitants of Delhi a 'mob', giving them a 'hellish aspect', and bringing in features of Indian city life which (though they might seem strange and threatening to Ehrlich) have little or nothing to do with 'over-population', this passage shows how subjective and how culturally or racially biased many neo-Malthusian arguments can be. If there were fleas hopping about in a New York taxi, would it prove the city overcrowded? Would people 'visiting, arguing and screaming' in Chicago or Seattle, or simply the presence there of 'people, people, people, people', make them living evidence of 'over-population'? The argument 'too many people' too often means in the

2. *How the Other Half Dies* (1986 edition), p. 67.

author's inner judgement too many of the *wrong sort* of people. It expresses a deeper repugnance and incomprehension, a failure to understand, even to accept the right to exist, of people of another race and culture.

The Malthusian or neo-Malthusian view has not gone uncontested, and the history, even the prehistory, of man has been sieved in search of counter-arguments and contrary evidence. Probably the most influential riposte has come from Ester Boserup in *The Conditions of Agricultural Growth* published in 1965. Boserup turns Malthus on his head, arguing that population pressure, rather than being a cause of demographic catastrophe, has been the driving force behind agricultural innovation and the greatest incentive for increased agrarian production. Far from being inelastic, as Malthus assumed, agriculture has expanded and adapted to meet the needs of a rising population. She states that the transition from pastoralism and shifting cultivation to various forms of increasingly more intensive agriculture (such as multiple cropping) was not due to free choice or random discovery, but arose from the pressure of demographic necessity. In contrast with those neo-Malthusians who see population growth as having disastrous consequences for the environment, through 'over-grazing', soil erosion, and the exhaustion of soil fertility through excessive cultivation, Boserup argues that the human contribution has generally been a constructive one. Although there have been ecological disasters in the past, in the main, man, she claims, has improved the productivity of the soil through the application of labour, through drainage, irrigation and the use of natural fertilizers and manure. Population growth, by this argument, has thus been the essential goad to agrarian innovation. It has been the stimulus, too, for the development of a more complex and technologically advanced society. Without a sufficiently high level of population, urbanization, state-formation, and industry would not have been possible. Faced with a choice between starvation and innovation, man, on balance, has opted for the latter and turned adversity to advantage.

Boserup's argument does not deny famine a place as either instrument or episode. Protracted food crises presumably served as the necessary incentive for agricultural innovation and prompted the transition from one form of production to another. And however successful a pre-industrial society might have been in maintaining a long-term balance between demographic change and subsistence needs, it would still, from time to time, have had to face temporary food shortages resulting from deficient harvests or the effects of warfare and pestilence. It must be wondered, though, whether historically human societies have had as much freedom to adapt and innovate as Boserup claims. There have been many societies (such as Ireland in the first half of the nineteenth century or China in the second) where, despite obvious and mounting demographic pressure, the necessary innovations or a more basic transformation of the agrarian system were precluded by political constraints, by a lack of capital or for want of the appropriate technological skills and knowledge, perhaps even by social and cultural factors. In such cases, famine appears as the almost unavoidable outcome of an apparently dead-end situation. Instead, the response of many societies in the past seems to have been to make a series of lateral shifts through various adaptive strategies – moving temporarily from pastoralism to raiding, for example, or falling back on wild game and forest fruits whenever sown crops failed – as a way of surviving a temporary or recurrent food crisis without taking the kind of innovative leap Boserup envisages. It would seem rash, therefore, to assume that historically societies had an almost indefinite capacity for change, or indeed even a willingness to do so given a powerful social and cultural commitment to a particular way of life and a particular means of subsistence. Proud pastoralists who despise the sedentary life, may, even in the worst famine situations, hold out for as long as possible against the pressure to become mere earth-bound tillers of the soil.

Malthus was surely wrong in postulating a single and universal law linking population and subsistence. But population growth, when treated not in isolation but in combination with technological stagnation, social conservatism and political inertia or oppression might form an integral part of the complex of forces responsible for famine causation.

Food entitlements and availability

There are other ways, too, in which the famine conundrum can be tackled. Many commentators have assumed, following Malthus's own reasoning, that a famine arises out of an actual shortfall in the means of subsistence. Either population in the long term outstrips the quantity of food available, or some 'natural disaster' occurs which destroys crops and stocks so that there is suddenly less food than usual to spread among the same number of people. Neo-Malthusian writers have often arrived at the conclusion that the stork has already sped past the plough (and thus that famine is sure to follow) simply by measuring global or Third World food stocks against rising population rates, without taking into account high levels of wasteful food consumption in the West, the nature of the foodstuffs produced (not everyone eats or wants to eat the same thing), and the unequal nature of food distribution (between nations and within states, classes and families).

In *Poverty and Famine*, published in 1981, the Indian economist Amartya Sen challenged the view that famines are caused by a 'food availability decline'. The critical issue for him is the way in which food is distributed rather than the volume of food itself. In Sen's words, starvation 'is the characteristic of some people not *having* enough to eat. It is not the characteristic of there *being* not enough to eat.' This assertion has global implications. Sen points out that agricultural production has kept pace with population growth in most parts of the world (Africa excepted) in recent decades: famines persist, however, because the food produced is not equitably shared out between countries or is not available to all who need it.

But Sen's main interest is in the way in which famines have been brought about locally through differential access to, and command over, available supplies of food. To explain this he develops a theory of 'exchange entitlements'. The term 'entitlement' is used to signify legally sanctioned and economically operative rights of access to resources that give control over food or can be exchanged for it. Through production, trade, and labour, through property rights and inheritance, or through the state's welfare provisions, individuals have access either to food itself or to the means by which to acquire it. Agricultural labourers earn money with which they buy their food or are paid in kind with wheat or rice. A landholder has the chance to exercise his entitlements either by selling the grain produced on his land or by consuming part of it himself. Entitlements are, therefore, not fixed and equal but vary according to an individual's position within a wider system of production, exchange, control and distribution. In consequence, when a famine situation arises the burden of deprivation and hunger is not evenly spread. Whatever may be the theoretical *per capita* availability of food, some social groups (seen by Sen as essentially occupational groups) will be unable to obtain sufficient food to meet their subsistence requirements because their entitlements have lost all or part of their value.

In the Bengal famine of 1943–44, which constitutes Sen's primary example, there was not, he argues, 'a serious shortage in the total supply of rice available for consumption in Bengal' as the official report of the 1944 Famine Inquiry Commission claimed. The rice harvest, he points out, was 13 per cent higher in 1942 than it had been

in 1941 and in that year there was no famine. But, due to the war
situation and the government's ineffective attempts to regulate supply
and control prices, the cost of rice and other essential commodities
rose sharply in 1942-43. Many labouring and artisanal groups in the
countryside lost their capacity to sell or exchange their labour and
goods in order to obtain food. The labourers either lost employment
altogether and so received no wages or the wages they did receive,
whether in cash or in kind, lagged far behind prices in value and
would not buy sufficient rice for their needs. Barbers, fishermen and
other rural specialists found that their services ceased to be in demand
or were rewarded at rates that no longer matched inflated price levels.
The food entitlement of labourers, Sen calculated, fell by a third in
1943 compared to what it had been in 1940. In real terms a haircut was
worth to the barber a fifth of what it had been three years earlier.
(Sen's observations on this point, it might be noted, are not entirely
new. During earlier famines in India the British were aware of the
early and acute distress experienced by rural and small-town weavers
whose market collapsed almost at the first hint of famine and for
whom special provision had to be made to save them from utter destitution.) Without an adequate system of state relief to compensate for
lost entitlements, agricultural labourers and artisans either died of
starvation in 1943 or were swept away in the epidemics that followed.
Farmers who could eat or sell what they had grown were, at least in
the short term, more favourably situated. Industrial workers and other
urban employees in Calcutta were protected by the relatively high
wages and subsidized rice that was specially provided for them. On
balance, then, it was not a decline in the actual volume of food that, in
Sen's view, caused the death of more than three million Bengalis in
1943-44, but differential access to food and a chronic loss of 'exchange
entitlements'.

Sen's hypothesis, elaborated through a series of examples taken from
more recent famines, has done much to revitalize and reorient the
discussion of famine. In particular it has drawn attention to famine's
uneven and discriminatory impact, though it has been left to others -
like Paul Greenough, writing on the same Bengal famine, and Megan
Vaughan in her study of the Malawi famine of 1949 - to pursue
further the question of which social elements are most adversely
affected and how precisely the burden of famine is distributed. But,
for all the unquestionable importance of his work, it must be doubted
whether Sen has really provided a theory of famine *causation*, as he
contends in challenging the 'food availability decline' argument, so
much as given an explanation of how famines develop once they have

(for whatever reason) been set in motion. As suggested at the start of this chapter, it would not be difficult to find examples of famines where there is clear evidence of a serious shortfall in food availability – whether due to adverse climate, insect pests and other causes, and where, because of transport difficulties or economic and political factors, there was little possibility of importing sufficient food to compensate for local losses. The Orissa famine of 1866, for example, resulted from a severely deficient rice harvest following years of heavy grain exports to other parts of eastern India. This left peasants without reserve food stocks to tide them over the crisis months. The consequences of drought were further exacerbated by the physical isolation of the area (the paucity of road and rail connections on the one hand, the effects of the monsoon winds on the other in closing Orissa's harbours to shipping during the height of the famine) and by the mistaken belief of the local administration that sufficient grain remained in the stricken districts in the hands of traders and speculators if it could only be flushed out and put on sale. The difficulty, as became tragically evident at the time, was not simply a lack of funds (or other entitlements) with which to buy grain or to earn it. There was a severe dearth of grain itself. Similarly, during the Chinese famine of 1876–79, the persistence of drought over several seasons so depleted the reserves and resources of even the relatively well-to-do peasant farmers that mass hunger and death resulted. The perilous state of the roads and the death of draught animals made it impossible to move grain in sufficient quantity from better-provisioned provinces and the ports to the needy interior districts.

The 'exchange entitlement' argument seems deficient in another respect, too. Sen explains how British wartime policies fuelled inflation and created a 'speculative spiral' of price rises, and no doubt this was a significant contributory factor. But he is also forced to admit that one of the impulses driving this inflation and speculation was an 'indifferent' winter crop in 1942 and a 'moderate short-fall in production' which by early 1943 had been translated into 'an exceptional short-fall in market release'. In fact these are the classic ingredients of famine in India and they probably hold an equal significance for many other times and places, too. A partial failure of the rains, a deficient crop yield, rumours of price rises – all these could have the effect, in a society where the subsistence basis of the mass of the population was already precarious and perhaps especially in an economy where the market played a critical part in meeting the subsistence needs of the poorer classes, of triggering alarm, sending prices soaring, and encouraging hoarding and speculation. As Richard

Cobb observed in the context of late eighteenth-century France in *The Police and the People*, 'the fear of dearth was permanent, especially at the lower levels of society, and it took very little at any time for this fear to become hysterical and to develop into the proportions of panic'. Hysteria, with its suggestion of an irrational or wildly exaggerated response, arguably overstates the case, for, as the same author elsewhere remarks, in dreading dearth and famine the common people were not living in a world of myth and unsubstantiated fear. They knew well enough from bitter experience that 'dearth and famine were in fact the greatest single threat to their existence'.

In seeking to explain why so many Bengalis starved in 1943–44, Sen says singularly little, too, about the long-term decline of agriculture in the province, the growing pressure on the land and the peasants' increasing burden of debt. All of these, taken together, made some kind of crisis, if not inevitable, then at least highly likely and much harder to resist once it began. Even the system of 'exchange entitlements' begs questions as to why certain sections of society were placed in such dependent and precarious relationships that even without a real decline in the actual availability of food they could still be left without either work or food. It might perhaps be suggested that Sen's theory, although certainly applied by him and by others to various famine contexts, has a particular significance for an agrarian society as highly differentiated and as elaborately stratified as that of nineteenth- and twentieth-century Bengal. All this suggests, then, the importance of looking at the long-term economic, social and political factors which made such a society so peculiarly fragile and vulnerable. One of the most effective ways of doing this is by looking at famine in the context of peasant societies as a whole.

3
Famine in Peasant Societies

Not all societies in history have shown an equal vulnerability to famine. As already suggested, this to some degree reflects climatic conditions and geographical location. Some human environments are innately more precarious than others: the risks attached to farming in the *sertão* of northeastern Brazil or on the floodplain of the Yangtse River in China are intrinsically greater than those associated with farming in Iowa or East Anglia. Rainfall may be less reliable; there may be a greater risk of inundation and drought; the soil may be poorer, less fertile or retentive of moisture. But other factors undoubtedly also play a part and can frequently be more decisive than climate or geography alone.

Adaptation and survival

Modern industrial societies, with their advanced technologies, their vast financial reserves and commercial resources, and their ready accessibility by road, rail and air, are largely immune to famine as a result of 'natural disasters'. Deficient harvests can be countered by moving surpluses from one place to another or by increasing the amount of food imported; and since agriculture anyway constitutes only part of a complex national and international economy, the employment and livelihood of a majority of the population remains largely unaffected by occasional poor harvests. In a country rich enough to buy its provisions in the supermarkets of world trade there is no need to maintain a Malthusian balance between a country's population and its agricultural output. Although a particularly long and severe winter or an excessively dry summer certainly affects levels of agricultural production, modern industrial societies are cushioned by their technology and affluence from major subsistence crises. Crop sprays, fertilizers, irrigation, efficient storage systems - all help to minimize the effects of erratic climate and crop pests. The prolonged drought England experienced in 1976, which a few centuries ago might have caused wholesale food shortages, was little more than a passing inconvenience to the public at large and no more than a temporary misfortune for the farmers themselves. No-one went hungry as a result. When crops do fail state subsidies and private insurance save modern farmers from most of the worst financial effects. A few farmers may go bankrupt, but they are unlikely to starve to death.

Vulnerability is more likely to be man-made. Invasion, civil war, and the accompanying political and administrative disruption or diversion of resources result in the breakdown of established patterns of food production and distribution. Embargoes, blockades and enemy attacks prevent the importation of alternative sources of supply. These are more likely causes of mass hunger than drought or an invasion of crop pests – unless in the future, as some ecologists predict, modern farming techniques fail to sustain their productivity, and the exhaustion of the soil, coupled with urban and industrial pollution, transforms what are now fertile fields into desert dustbowls.

At the opposite extreme, hunter-gatherers and nomadic pastoralists have probably been relatively free from famine. Although drought in the Sahel in the 1960s and 1970s has drawn attention to the plight of pastoralists on the margins of the Sahara, in general such forms of social organization can deploy a wide and effective range of adaptive strategies to enable them to survive. Mobility and a relatively low man/land ratio have always been among the nomads' greatest assets. When pastures dried up in one locality, they could pack up their tents and move to areas where the grass was still green or split up into smaller groups so as to disperse their animals over a wider grazing area. Part of the flock or herd was sold to purchase grain; other activities, including trade, assumed greater importance than usual (though in a situation of drought and hunger, the market becomes glutted with animals for sale and the terms of trade shift sharply away from the pastoralist). In some cases nomads driven by drought or by mounting population density from their accustomed pastures invaded and plundered their sedentary neighbours. The history of the steppes of central Asia and the Saharan fringes of western Africa is filled with examples of nomadic militancy. It testifies to the importance of such adaptive strategies for the nomads themselves and to the far-reaching effects of these periodic eruptions into the agrarian civilizations on their borders. But the response has not always been violent. The Tuaregs of the western Sahel accommodated themselves to their harsh and difficult environment by maintaining multiple political, social and economic relations with subordinate and neighbouring peoples, whose resources and food reserves they were entitled (to echo Sen) to call on when drought periodically dried up their grazing lands.

Hunter-gatherers also showed a remarkale capacity to adapt in the face of drought and to maintain adequate food supplies even at times when their sedentary neighbours were in the grip of severe food shortages. The Bushmen of the Kalahari still enjoy a comparatively healthy diet, drawn from a rich variety of plants as well as animals. Indeed, the sheer diversity of their food resources serves as a guarantee against sudden shortages: it is seldom that all their sources of supply fail even in the hardest seasons. They are largely free from the periods of seasonal hunger and the vitamin deficiencies that affect peasant cultivators in many parts of Africa. When prolonged droughts occur, the Bushmen respond by splitting up into smaller bands, by falling back on less preferred types of food, and by travelling as much as 200 miles a year in search of water and alternative food supplies. Again, mobility and a low density of population are critical to their survival.

Although there have been instances (such as among the nomadic tribes of Iran in 1870-71 and more recently in Ethiopia) where protracted drought and heavy stock losses have themselves been a cause of sedentization, in the main it was only when population increased without being able to find room for migration (or when freedom of movement was constricted by the encroachment of settled cultivation and the imposition of modern political boundaries), that the hunter-gatherers and pastoralists faced serious subsistence crises. It has been claimed that the shift to sedentary agriculture as the predominant means of subsistence over a large part of the globe during the so-called 'Neolithic revolution' was caused by increasing population densities making hunting and gathering impractical rather than by any sudden discovery of the advantages of sedentism. Pastoralists faced similar constrictions - as when nomads pressed in vain against the frontiers of the Roman or Chinese empires - but the threat to their survival has become most evident over the last century or so in Africa. The broad savanna lands once used by the Maasai and other pastoralists in Kenya and northern Tanzania for cattle grazing, hunting and raiding have steadily been whittled away by the encroachment of settled farming, even, latterly, by the establishment of game parks and wildlife reserves. Although the lordly Maasai found favour with Kenya's British rulers, many other pastoralist and nomadic people in Africa and Asia have been treated with great suspicion by colonial and post-colonial regimes. Branded as shiftless, even criminal, such groups have been pushed out of their traditional homelands often to accommodate peasant cultivators, who are regarded as more productive economically and politically more amenable. In West Africa the Tuaregs' desert-side economy was undermined by the incoming French colonial administration in the late nineteenth and early twentieth centuries. Their political ascendency (and hence their capacity to syphon off the resources of other communities in times of need) was overthrown; their flocks were pillaged to satisfy colonial demands for meat and skins; and their customary trade in salt and grain dwindled once the railways reoriented trade away from the desert to the coast. The marginalization of the nomads has greatly reduced their capacity to cope with periodic drought, and thus further hastens their decline and incorporation into sedentary agriculture or urban life. Ironically, nomadic pastoralism is an ecologically appropriate form of land-use in many semi-arid regions, and it has also proved an effective long-term subsistence strategy. The peasant farmers who displaced the nomads have frequently been less adaptive, less able to withstand prolonged drought, less in tune with the nature of the savanna environment.

Peasant societies

Those settled cultivators to whom we can apply the generic term 'peasants' have historically shown an exceptional vulnerability to famine. Indeed, if chronic hunger is likened to a disease, then it might be said to be endemic in most peasant societies for much of the time. As R. H. Tawney declared of China's peasants in the 1930s, famine for them was simply 'the last stage of a disease which, though not always conspicuous, is always present'. Or, as one British official remarked in India fifty years earlier: 'half of our agricultural population never know from year's end to year's end what it is to have their hunger fully satisfied'.

As the term peasant, for all its apparent familiarity, has been subject to considerable (and not always illuminating) academic debate, it is necessary to offer some explanation for its use. Peasants are small, usually family-oriented, agricultural producers, who own, rent, or hold through contract (for example as sharecroppers) the land they cultivate. With little or no capital at their disposal and a generally low level of technology, peasants rely on the land and their family's labour to meet household subsistence needs. Although the degree of internal stratification varies enormously, peasant societies are rarely free of some internal differences of wealth and access to the land. Peasant society has often been divided into three layers, and these internal divisions are of particular importance in understanding the differential impact of food crises and famines on rural households. Firstly, there are the rich peasants, who cultivate sufficient land to meet their own needs and may hire additional labour to help them to produce a marketable surplus; secondly, the middle peasants whose holdings are sufficient for their family subsistence needs but little more; and thirdly, the poor peasants who, holding insufficient land to satisfy their needs, have to find employment as labourers on the lands of others or perhaps outside the village as seasonal and plantation workers. In practice, as anyone acquainted with peasant society will readily attest, these differences are seldom clear-cut; but they do suggest that, within the confines of peasant society, there exist significant if not always conspicuous differences. Each section of the peasantry has, as Sen would put it, different 'entitlements'.

Although rich peasants are in some contexts a transitional group, moving away from a largely subsistence agriculture to fuller involvement in a market economy and thus towards becoming commercial or capitalist farmers, most writers stress the extent to which peasants are agricultural producers working essentially in order to meet their own needs rather than as businessmen intent on maximizing their profits. But the degree of peasant commitment to the market is itself an important variable. Peasants have generally had to depend on some form of marketing or exchange to acquire goods they cannot grow or produce themselves, whether basic items like salt or iron implements or perhaps non-essentials like tobacco. In present-day Africa or India, many peasants have a high level of market involvement and operate as small-scale commodity producers, growing coffee, cocoa or rice for sale and not for consumption. Formerly, however, before the development of effective transport systems to incorporate peasant households into a wider, and ultimately international, market economy, peasant production was by necessity as much as by inclination far less market-oriented. There has been much discussion in recent years of whether peasants are wary of markets and reluctant to be drawn away from their subsistence base or whether they are anxious to seek out market opportunities and to respond to wider economic forces. Generalizations seem difficult and peasant attitudes have no doubt varied from one society to another and according to different political and economic contexts. But certainly the involvement of peasants in market economies, as already hinted in the previous chapter, can be a critical factor in their responses to incipient food shortages and in their structural or long-term vulnerability to famine.

By extension, the term 'peasant society' can be applied to cover not just the peasant cultivators themselves but also the landless agricultural labourers (sometimes merged with the poor peasants or treated as a fourth subdivision of the peasantry and in some cases present in the form of serfs and bonded labour), and the village artisans and menials (local shepherds, weavers, and potters for example) with whom the peasants have close social ties and exchange goods and services. Together these generally village-based groups – the cultivators, labourers and craft or occupational specialists – constitute the numerically dominant but socially and politically subordinate strata of a wider social order.

In their attempts to define what constitutes a peasant society the anthropologists Eric Wolf and George M. Foster both stress the incorporation of peasants into a wider social hierarchy, with a political structure and a market organization: these latter being commonly represented by an elite (the nobility or the landlord class), the state and the city. In Wolf's judgement this subordination of the peasantry is a central aspect of its identity. Hence 'it is only when a cultivator is integrated into a society with a state – that is, when the cultivator becomes subject to the demands and sanctions of power-holders outside his social stratum – that we can appropriately speak of peasantry'. Because the peasants are 'subject to asymmetrical power relations which make a permanent charge on [their] production', they have, Foster claims, very little control over the conditions that govern their lives. Not only are they poor: they are also 'relatively powerless'. The common assumption that peasants are self-sufficient producers and consumers (and thus purely 'subsistence farmers'), therefore needs substantial qualification in the light of their political and social subordination and the extent of their wider economic ties. They do not have unfettered control over their own forces of production. To quote Foster again, 'whatever the form of control held by the elite, they usually drain off most of the economic surplus a peasant creates, beyond that necessary for a bare subsistence living and for local religious expenditures'.

The idea of peasants as 'relatively powerless' is critical to the discussion that follows. In part it needs qualification, especially if it is taken to imply mere passivity and inertia on the part of the peasants and a total incapacity to affect their social conditions and material environment. But their political subordination and the appropriation of their surplus by others are cardinal features of the peasants' predicament, and help, it will be argued, to explain their particular vulnerability to famine.

Whereas population densities in hunting, gathering and herding communities necessarily remain relatively low, peasant societies, with their heavy reliance upon cereal and root crops and with animals occupying only a secondary role (as draught animals, scavengers and an occasional additional source of protein), can sustain far higher man/land ratios. A square kilometre of land which might support only four hunter-gatherers could provide sustenance for up to 250 cultivators under a system of annual cropping and as many as 500 or more if the land were brought under multiple cropping to yield two, perhaps even three, crops a year. As Boserup pointed out, multiple cropping is one of the most effective ways in which productivity can be increased to support a rising density of population. In the 1930s some parts of the lower Yangtse valley in China recorded population levels in excess of 2,000 people per square mile, and multiple-cropping rice cultivation in other parts of Asia, such as Bengal or Java, has produced similar or even higher densities. Without fresh lands to exploit by more extensive means and through the development of ever more intensive cultivation techniques, a process characterized by Clifford Geertz as 'agricultural involution', peasant agriculture has been able to sustain ever-greater numbers. Irrigated rice cultivation particularly lends itself to this process, as Geertz explained in the case of modern Java:

> In addition to improving the general irrigation system within which a terrace is set, the output of most terraces can be almost indefinitely increased by more careful, fine-comb cultivation techniques; it seems almost always possible somehow to squeeze just a little more out of even a mediocre *sawah* [wet-rice field] by working it just a bit harder. . . . The capacity of most terraces to respond to loving care is amazing.[1]

Given the right soils and climate, peasant cultivation, whether in Java, or in parts of China, India, mainland Southeast Asia, or medieval Europe, has often attained an almost horticultural intensity – gardening, as it were, without the flowers.

But for all its skill and success in wresting sustenance from the soil and in supporting extraordinarily high densities of population, peasant agriculture has been subject to all the hazards predatory man and capricious nature can hurl at it. Densely packed peasant communities are more vulnerable to communicable diseases than scattered bands of nomads, their crowded villages and irrigated fields a host to rats, fleas, and water-borne epidemics. It was probably through the domestication of animals in early human settlements that diseases like

1. Geertz, *Agricultural Involution*, p. 35.

smallpox began to circulate among people instead of their original animal hosts. Reliance upon a single staple, like the Irish potato, creates extreme vulnerability to the effects of crop disease. A single blight and, as in Ireland, the entire food source of a third or more of the population is lost almost over night. And although the potato happens to be rich in nutrients (one explanation for the rapid rise in Ireland's population in the eighteenth and early nineteenth centuries), many other peasant staples, such as maize, in the long term undermine health when not used as part of a more varied diet. They cause serious vitamin deficiencies (and diseases such as pellagra), thus weakening resistance to epidemics and the effects of prolonged hunger. The malnutrition persistent in many peasant populations even in times of relative plenty helped swell the heavy death tolls when famine struck.

The short-fallow system employed in medieval Europe, with its year-long dependence upon the produce of a single grain harvest, asked too much of the beneficence of the heavens and left the peasants with too little to fall back on in the event of droughts or storms. The peasants who crowded onto the silt-rich, water-abundant margins of the Ganges delta or the Yangtse river banks exposed themselves to the periodic perils of floods, crop destruction and heavy loss of life. As peasant densities rose and the hills and valleys were stripped of their tree cover, the risk of soil erosion and inundation multiplied. Peasants were left without forest larders to turn to when their own cupboards were bare, without woodlands in which to graze a few goats or pigs to supplement their meagre diet and income. The diversity of food resources that sustained hunter-gatherers through times of drought was lost once peasant agriculture cast its close-patterned counterpane over the landscape. By their populousness and by their quest for a living scratched from even the most forbidding soil, peasants pushed against the very margins of subsistence, risking death not just in their tens and hundreds like nomads but in their millions. Paradoxically, peasants, one of the most long-lived forms of human organization known to recorded history, seem always to walk a razor-thin line between survival and extinction.

Without capital and with the benefit of only minimal levels of technology, peasant inputs into agriculture were mainly in terms of their own labour. By an arduous application of time and physical energy, through what has aptly been called 'self-exploitation', peasants wrested improvements from the soil too slight and marginal to attract any profit-minded capitalist farmer. But the technological limitations and slender resource base that plagued peasant societies is borne out by the almost universal phenomenon of the 'hungry gap'. This occurred every year between the exhaustion of the previous harvest and the ripening of the new crops. It was hardly ever due to lack of effort or foresight. No-one chose to be hungry for two or three months of the year, especially as the *soudure* (as it has been known to the French-speaking world) left peasants physically weakest at the very time when they needed to muster fresh energy for ploughing and planting the new season's crops. Part of the explanation for these annual shortages lay with the operation of the tax system and market economy. Peasants commonly had to sell a large part of their crop at harvest time (when prices tended to be low due to the abundance of food) in order to raise the cash required to pay their tax demand. If they then needed to buy back grain later in the year, they could only do so when grain was becoming scarce, prices were rising and traders and moneylenders demanded high rates of interest for a loan. The alternative was to try to subsist on as little as possible during the lean months of the year, thus economizing on both consumption and expenditure.

There were problems, too, of storage. Some staples, like potatoes, could not be kept, even in earth clamps, for as long as a year before rotting and becoming an inedible mess. July and August were accordingly the 'meal months' for Ireland's peasantry, trying to eke out a living on other foodstuffs until the new potato crop was ready to harvest. Other staples, and it was one of the historic attractions of cereal crops, could be stored for far longer periods in specially constructed grain pits and granaries, but were seldom free of the rodents and insects' heavy levy. More often the land, with the primitive levels of technology available and without sufficient fallowing or application of manure to restore and maintain its fertility (there is some evidence to suggest that cereal yields were falling in western Europe during the course of the Middle Ages as a result), simply produced too little to sustain a peasant household from one harvest to the next, especially when a large part of the harvest went to nourish the landlord, sustain the clergy and uphold the state. For some peasants a winter of idleness, with social and ceremonial expenditures pared to a bare minimum, was the only way to survive this lean and hungry time and conserve enough energy for the ploughing and sowing to follow. To increase productivity by bringing new land under cultivation or planting additional crops, where this was even permitted or technically feasible, often only meant making a present of the peasant's extra labour to an exacting landlord or an assertive rich peasant. There might be as little incentive for improvement as their was means for effecting it.

Unlike pastoralists, too, peasants were mostly 'earth-bound', tied to the soil by custom, obligation and necessity. Peasants did migrate (not least under pressure of hunger), but commitment to the land, generally to a particular plot of land, limited peasant adaptability in a crisis, and made them more obliged to accept external authority, exploitation and control. The peasant could not, like the pastoralist, drive his assets elsewhere or, most times, simply pick up his belongings and leave. A peasant who fled in the face of famine, an invading army or landlord oppression left behind him the principal, perhaps even the only, means of earning a livelihood.

Subsistence and subordination

In the nineteenth century peasants were often spoken about in stridently negative and unsympathetic terms. The seemingly timeless character of their way of life (in an age that prided itself on dynamic change) and their closeness to a primitive nature, made them appear anachronistic, even suspect, in the eyes of the city-dwelling middle classes and intelligentsia, seemed to set them in opposition to the momentous forces of historical change that were transforming Europe. Karl Marx, who, for all his undoubted sympathy for other sections of the working population, seemed particularly anxious to see them carted off to the graveyards of history so as to free Europe to pursue its revolutionary destiny, once described peasants as the 'force that represents barbarism in civilization'. Deploring their lack of class identity and cohesion, he dubbed them 'potatoes in a sack', a collection of self-sufficient households whose interests, though mutual, could 'beget no community, no national bond and no political organization'.

This hostile view of the peasantry has inevitably spilt over into the discussion of famine in peasant societies as well. Famines have frequently been attributed not to external forces, whether of man or nature, imposing themselves upon the peasantry, but to the peasants' own intrinsic weaknesses, to their deficient social and economic values and what are seen to be typically peasant characteristics of indolence and improvidence. Malthus, albeit from a vastly different ideological standpoint, shared something of Marx's disparaging view of the peasantry. Although he surveyed a great array of different societies in his *Essay on the Principle of Population*, peasants were singled out as possessing some of mankind's most undesirable attributes. In his brief commentary on Ireland, for instance, Malthus noted the ease with which that 'nourishing root', the potato, could be grown in sufficient quantities to provide for a family's subsistence needs. But this, he claimed, merely brought out the worst in the Irish peasantry, for, when 'joined to the ignorance and depressed state of the people', the potato's plenty simply 'prompted them to follow their [reproductive] inclinations with no other prospect than an immediate bare subsistence'. In this manner the population, 'pushed much beyond the industry and present resources of the country', was already by the turn of century on the slippery slope towards famine. Malthus characteristically made no mention either of the conditions of tenancy or the wider social and political conditions that were helping to create in Ireland such an 'impoverished and miserable state'. He dwelled instead upon what he took to be the innate character of the peasant poor, the almost lemming-like self-destructive 'inclinations' that hurled the 'lower classes of the people' over the precipice of hunger and want.

Where Malthus left off, Ronald E. Seavoy, in his recent book *Famine in Peasant Societies*, has gamely followed on. He rounds on peasants, past and present, for what he calls the 'indolence ethic' that makes them habitually subject to famine and prevents them from matching their numbers to an assured food supply. Singling out for comment Indonesian agriculture in general (an improbable choice one would think after Geertz's description of 'fine-comb cultivation techniques') and the famine crises in Ireland in the 1840s and India in the 1870s, he argues that in their desire to expend as little labour as possible peasants grow only enough food to provide for their immediate subsistence needs. Thus peasants (characterized here as essentially constituting 'subsistence cultures') take a calculated risk, a 'subsistence compromise' Seavoy calls it, gambling on growing 'sufficient food for their own consumption with the least expenditure of labour on the assumption that all crop years will be normal'. In consequence, when, contrary to their lazy presumption, crops even partly fail peasants are almost immediately reduced to a starvation level. Even the high birth-rate, which Seavoy sweepingly and quite inaccurately attributes to 'all known peasant societies', is accounted for by the peasants' desire to escape from the irksome labour of ploughing and reaping as quickly as possible. Apparently, the sooner they can transfer this onerous burden onto their children and retire to the comfort of their firesides the better!

Having diagnosed this prevalent malaise in peasant societies, Seavoy is not slow to recommend a cure. The remedy for peasant indolence and famine vulnerability, according to the author, is greater involvement in a market economy, if necessary through the forcible intervention of the state. Only by this means, it is claimed, were first England and then Ireland (through the trauma of the Great Famine) able to escape from the perennial threat of hunger to find a more secure subsistence. Obliging peasants to become profit-minded farmers instead of subsistence-minded peasants, would, it is argued, lead to increased output and draw them into a network of production and exchange capable of sustaining them despite periodic droughts and crop failures.

The argument is certainly not devoid of all value. It gives due emphasis to an inherent frailty in peasant economies. It illustrates how historically the dissolution of peasant society through a process of capitalist transformation has been one of the routes by which recurrent famine has been evaded or overcome. But, as an argument for explaining peasant vulnerability to famine it is short-sighted, superficial and almost abusive in its failure to comprehend peasant dilemmas and constraints. Minimizing labour inputs is not an objective unique to peasant households: it exists in many different forms of social and economic organization from hunter-gatherers to our own hi-tech, labour-saving age. Why single out peasants for this apparent mark of disapprobation? And though different climates, different systems of agriculture, and different staples required different inputs of labour – the demands of the Irish potato crop were notoriously and quite exceptionally low – where irrigated cereal crops have been concerned, especially multiple-cropping rice cultivation, peasant agriculture is extremely exacting, involving long hours of work spread over a large part of the year. Hard work and thrift are more common and prestigious peasant values than indolence and profligacy as any acquaintance with the peasants of India and China would quickly show. Seavoy has made the mistake of adopting the terminology of the elites, indigenous and foreign, landlords, colonial officials and the like, for whom 'indolence' was the mark of the peasant beast. Contrasting the 'proverbial lassitude' or 'fecklessness' of the Irish with the self-declared energy and enterprise of the 'naturally industrious' Anglo-Saxon was one of the ways in which English contemporaries sought to explain away the Irish crisis of the 1840s. It saved them from having to search out reasons that were deeper and more complex. The myth of the 'lazy native' was similarly one of the stock stereotypes of colonial rule in Africa and Asia, propounded by Europeans who saw no merit in local cultural values (including those which sanctioned the conservation of human energy in times of low food availability) and understood little of the practical hazards of farming in a tropic environment.

It is also hard to accept that peasants were so blindly indolent or fatalistic as not to guard against the possibility (indeed, in India's case, the recurrent probability) of periodic drought and crop failure – unless there were powerful reasons why they were unable to do so. Seavoy's argument presumes, all too uncritically, that peasants have the freedom to control and so to change the economic and social conditions in which they live. In effect, the peasants are blamed for what they are 'relatively powerless' to alter in their own lives. Treating peasants as if they were autonomous farmers, geared only to self-sufficiency, not only overlooks the extent to which most peasants are already involved in some degree in market relations. It also ignores one of the peasantry's cardinal characteristics – their subordination to the holders of economic and political power. And it has often been this factor above all others that has served to transform an otherwise endurable 'natural disaster' into the collective catastrophe of famine.

Peasant vulnerability to famine was not a self-induced nightmare, but a spectre present in the very structure of the agrarian order within which they were confined. As A. L. Kroeber reminds us, peasants constitute 'part societies'; they form a 'class segment of a larger population'. Historically, free peasants – peasants without masters – have been rare, except in frontier situations. Far more commonly they have been subordinated to landlords, to the state, and often to the Church as well, and each of these demanded and exacted some kind of payment – whether in the form of goods produced, cash or labour – from the peasant household. A quarter, a third, even a half – the percentage of the peasants' produce taken varied greatly from one society to another and one time to another. Peasants might also be obliged to work on their lord's land, often at times of the year when they would rather be ploughing, sowing and reaping for themselves. They might, under one compulsion or another, be conscripted into an army, or, in modern times, be inducted into a plantation or factory work-force with consequences no less deleterious for the family's subsistence requirements. The peasant had also to meet other demands on the harvest – for seed grain for the next season's sowing (which might in itself in a low-yielding agricultural system swallow up a quarter or a fifth of the annual produce), or to feed draught animals. Funds had to be found, too, to pay for ceremonial expenses, such as weddings, funerals and the festivals of the peasant year. To the outside observer these last might seemingly smack of peasant profligacy. But they were necessary for the renewal of social ties and as the price of membership of a wider community which (looked at purely materially) might in turn provide support in times of need or in old age. Given, too, the peasants' faith in good fortune and the fertility of womenfolk, animals, and fields as in the gift of the gods, contributing to feasts, festivals and propitiatory rites was a logical way of investing in the household's future.

By the sweat of their labour peasants underwrote the sweet-smelling civilizations of the pre-industrial world. The rice, maize and corn they produced (commodities that could be transported, stored and substituted for money) fed the hungry rise of cities, nourished empires, provisioned bureaucracies and armies, enabled civilizations to develop with sufficient wealth and security from want to afford literati and cultured elites. The vast quantities of rice exacted as tribute from the paddylands of the lower Yangtse fed Peking, with its million or more inhabitants, and allowed the hub of the Chinese imperial system to function effectively. Not surprisingly, peasants were viewed as the ultimate mainstay of China's economy and civilization. The peasants' labour provided the state with its basic 'fund of power', and the survival of the pre-modern state system depended largely upon its capacity to draw off sufficient surplus from the peasantry to meet its own operational needs. The state thus had a vested interest in the preservation of the peasantry and in its replication. By encouraging the settlement of new lands, the draining of marshes and the felling of forests, by promoting emigration to under-populated regions (or those whose populations had been depleted by war and famine), the state and the nobility saw ways of turning the land to more productive use and swelling their own revenues. Peasant societies not only multiplied through their own agricultural colonization and sexual reproduction, but also through the encouragement of self-interested masters.

It could be said that this gave the state and the nobility a vested interest in the peasants' welfare and security of subsistence as well, and up to a point this was probably so. It has been argued that many pre-modern or pre-colonial regimes acknowledged peasants' subsistence needs, remitting taxes in times of bad harvests, and never taking more than the peasant household needed to survive till the next harvest. This kind of respect for the cultivators' basic needs formed part of the theory of kingship in many parts of the world, part of a hypothetical transaction by which peasants voluntarily surrendered a share of their hard-won product in exchange for royal protection and support in times of need. Indeed, it is possible to advance a theory of the origins of feudalism in western Europe in the early Middle Ages in precisely these terms. Peasants, it could be argued, living in a troubled and uncertain age, accepted feudal subordination and a duty to provision their masters in exchange for security from invasion and arbitrary taxation and, in an era of low and uncertain yields, for the gift of food in times of extreme dearth. In practice, one must doubt that there was ever such an equitable and mutually agreed transaction. Monarchs, nobles and seigneurial lords often responded to purely pragmatic needs and tended to neglect theoretical obligations and cultural commandments. For every good king who entered folk memory as the provider of his people, there was at least one bad one who 'ate up' the peasants with his exactions. Relying upon the apparent 'docility' of the peasants, their lack of arms, organization and leadership, or simply upon raw coercive power, emperors, kings and nobles seized as much as they could or dared from the cultivating classes. Illicit levies - whether by venal officials, predatory bandits, or marauding armies - further increased the peasants' back-breaking burden. Even in the best of times, peasants received precious little protection or charity in return for their taxes. Peasants continued to exist (or were encouraged or allowed to do so), but only, in a great many cases, by the slenderest of margins. Thus when war, flood, famine and pestilence came they were ill-equipped to survive them. As Tawney said of China's peasants, the position of the rural population was 'that of a man standing permanently up to his neck in water, so that even a ripple is sufficient to drown him'.

The limits to peasant adaptation

This is not, however, to suggest that peasants have always been historically immobile and utterly without power to affect their own fortunes. There have been a variety of ways in which peasants have increased agricultural productivity and found ways to provide a more secure subsistence base or to feed a larger population, free, at least in the short term, from the threat of mass starvation. But, once again, at issue here is not just the immediate question - can peasants feed themselves and avert famine? There is also the broader question of how we are to understand peasants in history - whether as the indolent 'victims' of history, supine even in the face of the gravest misfortune, or as a more dynamic and purposeful force of agrarian change. Seen in this context, famine serves as a measure of peasants' adaptability or inertia, as a means of gauging their ability (or otherwise) to control and alter the terms of their own predicament.

Let us begin with a positive endorsement of peasant enterprise and innovation. David Ludden in his recently published account of peasant history in the Tirunelveli district of South India has argued powerfully for a theory of peasant dynamism. Over the span of a thousand years from 900 to 1900 he sees peasants as important instigators of agrarian change and as significant participants in creating and maintaining sophisticated systems of political organization and economic exchange. Civilization, in Ludden's view, was not something thrust upon a barbaric and unchanging peasantry from on high. It grew up from below, nurtured by the peasants themselves and over many generations, through their skilful manipulation of the local environment and its agricultural potential. Through a gradually accumulated knowledge of plants, soils and seasons, they were able to wrest a living from even the most parched and miserly tracts. One of the earliest and most significant developments in an area where rainfall was sparse and erratic was the construction of irrigation works along the Tambraparni river, the only perennial river in the district. Early irrigation works were primitive earth dams, in time replaced by an extensive network of masonry dams and an elaborate system of distribution channels. Even away from the Tambraparni, man-made reservoirs frugally conserved the scant rainfall and, along with wells, watered precious patches of irrigated crops. But it was double-cropping along the Tambraparni that gave Tirunelveli its rice surplus to support the growth of a literate culture and establish wider political and commercial systems: paddy formed the basis for trade as well as tribute.

Less favoured by natural water resources, peasants in other parts of Tirunelveli district, through a long process of adaptation and experimentation, devised their own ways of augmenting agricultural production. On the dry, infertile soils of the southeast, a community known as the Shanars learned to cultivate and exploit the palmyra (an unprepossessing tree that looks more like a well-used paint-brush than the customary image of a stately palm) as a source of sugar and fermented liquor, and as material for thatching, basket-making and matting. The palmyra's suitability to the local soils and climate helped establish the Shanars as traders as well as toddy-tappers. In the district's black-soil areas immigrants from the Telugu-speaking areas further north brought agricultural skills unfamiliar to the local Tamil population, specializing in the growing of cotton and other market crops. The district's dry soils were also skilfully husbanded to raise plantains, pulses and oil-seeds. With patience and perseverance even the most forbidding soil could be persuaded to yield a crop, even if only the coarse-grained millets that served as the staple diet of the rural labourers and poor peasants. Coastal contact with the Portuguese in the sixteenth century brought in new crops from the Americas to add to the great variety already produced locally – tobacco, for instance, and the chillies that breathed fire into local curries and chutneys. Through their intimate knowledge of their surroundings and resources peasants learned over time to shape their own environment and to fashion for themselves a viable subsistence. Drought and famine could not be entirely banished, but Ludden (like Boserup) sees agriculture as capable of an almost endless series of adaptations and innovations, making ever more effective use of a finite quantity of available land.

According to Ludden's account, too, the advent of British rule in 1801 did not halt the advance of Tirunelveli's peasant agriculture. On the contrary, by improving roads and building railways, and by expanding overseas trade, especially in the district's prized raw cotton, the British created vastly increased market opportunities for the district's peasant producers. Famine, no more than in the pre-colonial past, could not be altogether excluded – Tirunelveli was one of the south Indian districts hard hit by the famine of 1876–78 – but the peasants' capacity for survival had been greatly augmented by their positive response to the fresh opportunities opened up by colonialism. Moreover, to the peasants' own agricultural production were added the advantages of expanding participation in trade, which further diminished the dangers of local food shortages. In marked contrast to Seavoy's stereotype of a constricting and ineffective bid for self-sufficiency, the peasants of Ludden's Tirunelveli were bound by commercial, political, and social ties into wider, protective systems of exchange and distribution. A peasant household's ability to feed itself and avert hunger was, therefore, also a product of multiple social and economic ties ranging far beyond the peasants' own immediate locality.

In broad terms Ludden's account of Tirunelveli district could be repeated for the history of peasant agriculture in many other parts of the pre-industrial world. There are many similarities, for example, with the history of medieval Europe, though the precise forms of adaptation and innovation necessarily varied in their character and emphases from one region to another. Talk of indolence and passivity seems in this context to be singularly out of place. Apparently tradition-bound and innately conservative when intercepted at a single moment in time, peasants appear over a broad sweep of history to be rather more than its abject minions. Taken in the long term they busily transform the landscape and by their labour and inventiveness refashion it to satisfy increasing needs.

However, it may be doubted that peasants invariably enjoyed the

range of almost limitless opportunities Ludden describes or the
freedom to enjoy the fruits of their own labour he appears to attribute
to them. Most discussions of peasant agriculture go rather further in
weighing up peasants' energy and adaptation against their technical
and political limitations. Where Ludden's peasants appear as a hardy
race of free farmers and frontier pioneers, transforming unruly
wilderness into a nature that was dutiful as well bountiful, more
commonly the tale is of the stark compromises forced upon peasant
agriculture by the demands of the elite, by the niggardliness of nature,
and by the limitations of a primitive technology.

Peasant agriculture in China perhaps gives a more reliable impression of an uneasy balance between adaptation and stagnation,
dynamism and constraint. Faced with the repeated threat of famine,
China's peasants developed many new varieties of rice. Some, like the
celebrated Champa rice which originated in southeast Asia, were well-
suited to double-cropping, and could produce a good yield even in a
short growing season. Others, like the variety appropriately known
as 'rescue from famine', could be planted when other crops had
withered from drought or been washed away in a flood. Between the
fourteenth and twentieth centuries China staged a 'green revolution'
of its own: rice yields doubled, mainly through the selection of better
seeds, the spread of higher-yielding varieties, and the increased use of
irrigation. The state, nowhere more peasant-conscious than in China,
played its part in accelerating this process of innovation and expansion. Directly, or through officials and the gentry, it encouraged the
introduction of new varieties of rice, supervised irrigation works, and
fostered emigration to thinly populated border areas, like Yunnan in the
southwest and Manchuria in the northeast. American foodstuffs had
their bounty for Chinese agriculture as for that of India, Africa and
Europe. Groundnuts, maize and sweet potatoes grew on soils too thin
or rocky to suit rice or wheat cultivation. This increased crop variety
and raised productivity on such a scale that it is said to have
contributed significantly to China's rapid population growth between
1644 and 1911, the period of Manchu rule. From 150 million people
at the start of the eighteenth century, China raced to 300 million a
century later. Where in the late Middle Ages a hungry Europe looked
beyond its own frontiers for food and wealth and embarked on a global
Age of Discovery, China exploited ever more intensively the riches of
its own soil. A hectare of land in early modern China, Pierre Chaunu
has pointed out, could support twenty to twenty-five times as many
people as the same area in Europe: 'Europe wasted her space', while
China's growing millions were supported by an ever more intensive

exploitation of the soil. But, long-term, there was a high price to pay.

Increased food production may well have fuelled population growth or, conversely, if we follow Boserup's argument, the rapid rise in population may have provided the necessary stimulus for agricultural expansion and innovation – the two are in practice difficult to distinguish. Whichever was the case, by the early and middle decades of the nineteenth century China was entering a protracted food crisis, quite unlike the temporary effects of a single bad harvest brought on by drought or flood. Histories compiled by the gentry of the rice-bowl provinces of the lower Yangtse in the first half of the century indicate that peasants' living standards were falling sharply, making it difficult for them to maintain even a basic level of subsistence. It was not just that population, Malthusian-style, was outstripping food production. China's crisis was deepened by the decline of the Manchu dynasty with all that this connoted for the maintenance of administrative efficiency and for peasant security – from a dwindling ability to control banditry and crush rebellion, to the silting up of the Grand Canal (the main artery of the imperial tribute system) and the neglect of irrigation works and flood control measures. The Taiping rebellion of 1851–64, itself the bitter fruit of peasant landlessness and hunger, failed to topple the Manchus from the imperial throne, but plunged China into the bloodiest civil war in history. It left an estimated twenty million people dead in its terrible wake. Yet even this most gargantuan of 'positive checks', which, with the accompanying famines, left some areas of China depopulated for decades afterwards, failed to resolve the country's deeper malaise. Nor could the other famines that followed afterwards, at such cost to Chinese life, in the tortured century between the Taiping rebellion and the communist takeover of 1949. Politically and technologically Chinese agriculture was so far sunk in crisis that only a transformation of the entire agrarian system (and not a succession of Malthusian purges) could free it from its structural difficulties and dilemmas.

The fate of the Taipings is illustrative of a second aspect of the problem. With their utopian programme of land-sharing and a common granary, the Taipings demonstrated the peasants' urgent appetite for change. But their defeat was a reminder of the repeated inability of peasants (not just in China alone) to change the political order by and for themselves or struggle free from their customary subordination to the gentry and the state. Even when in a rare moment, as at the birth of the Ming dynasty in the 1360s, China's peasants combined with dissident gentry to defeat a reigning dynasty, they were unable to replace it by a more equitable order. A dynasty, new in name but ancient in form, arose phoenix-like from the ashes of the old. Until 1911, through all the cycles of dynastic change, the imperial order always contrived to successfully re-establish itself. As a highly effective means of extracting surplus from the peasants it was not readily made historically redundant. In China, as in medieval Europe and elsewhere, peasants lacked the political power, and often, too, the political leadership and vision, to dismantle the old order and usher in a revolutionary new age. For as long as this continued to be the case the material conditions of the peasants, and their underlying vulnerability to famine, were likely to remain basically unaltered.

The background to famine in Ireland in the 1840s, Russia in the 1890s, or Bengal in the 1940s, reveals similar patterns of narrowing peasant opportunity and inability to act or innovate on a scale sufficient to avoid the onset of famine.

In Ireland, as in China, population growth was one obvious ingredient in the 'Great Hunger' of the 1840s, but it was by no means the only factor involved. The Act of Union of 1801, which brought Ireland under the direct authority of the Parliament at Westminster, enabled Irish interests to be sacrificed to those of an England that was economically and politically infinitely more powerful. The Anglo-Irish landlords, some (though not all) of them absentees, lacked either the enthusiasm or the capital to develop their estates along the lines of England's Agricultural Revolution. Only in the east, where Irish agriculture lay in closest proximity to English markets, were there signs of a move towards capital-intensive farming before the famine. Instead of consolidation after the model of the English enclosures, there was a reckless division of arable land into smaller and smaller plots, until by the 1830s three-quarters of the land-holdings were of 20 acres or less and half of under ten acres. Only by relying almost exclusively on potatoes – a third of the population were said to be solely dependent on the crop by the mid-1840s – were the peasants able to scratch a living from their handkerchief-sized holdings. There was little inducement for peasants to improve their holdings. Any improvements made would lead to an increased rent demand or the transfer of the land to a tenant willing, in sheer desperation, to pay an even higher rent. As so often the case, peasant was in competition with peasant to gain access to the soil – to the ultimate advantage of neither. Unlike in England, too, there was a lack of industry and urban employment to absorb a population which had roughly doubled between 1780 and 1841 to just over 8 million, but which retained one of the highest rural population densities to be found anywhere in Europe.

Even in this bleak prospect there were a few signs of attempted adaptation. It has been suggested, for example, that the rate of population increase was already beginning to slow down before the famine struck (though too much hangs upon interpretation of the early nineteenth century censuses for any definitive statements to be made on this point), and increasing numbers of poor peasants were seeking a partial escape through seasonal migration to the fields and factories of England. But Irish agriculture was too anachronistic and impoverished to withstand the pressures of increasing population, especially when these were coupled with the constraints of political domination. Although there were evident signs of unrest, both in the agitation for the repeal of the Act of Union and in the sporadic agrarian 'outrages' of the Whiteboys and similar movements, these were palpably insufficient to force an uninterested British public and a prejudiced Parliament to favour the drastic change in Ireland that alone might have saved the peasants from the looming crisis.

In Russia the developments which led to the famine of 1891-92 were also long in the making, and had deep structural roots. Population growth was undeniably a factor in increasing pressure on the land and in the fifty provinces of European Russia population shot up from some 50 million in 1860 to around 80 million by the end of the century. But in the estimation of most historians demographic increase was secondary to the political and economic obstacles that beset peasant society in late Tsarist Russia. The emancipation of the serfs in 1861 had left the peasants in an unpromising position. Burdened with heavy taxation and annual redemption payments for the land they had acquired, with opportunities for agricultural development inhibited by inadequate resources and the low level of agricultural technology, and lacking the stimulus of large urban markets for their produce, the peasants were confined to a slight and, in many cases, narrowing margin of subsistence. On top of this came falling international grain prices in the 1880s (a reminder that involvement in a wider market was not every peasant's panacea). For the sake of short-term financial gain and to prop up the ailing Tsarist state, I. A. Vyshnegradskii as Minister of Finance, forced peasants (with the slogan 'we may not eat enough, but we will export') to surrender yet more of their meagre harvest. A decreasing percentage of peasants could afford to maintain any livestock and draught animals; more and more they sold wheat to buy rye and other cheaper grains for their own consumption. These were among the visible signs of a growing destitution, which left peasants hazardously exposed and physically weakened. When, in 1891, drought and a poor harvest occurred over a large part of central Russia and the Volga region, the 'overburdened peasants and their exploited fields could take no more', and mass hunger quickly followed.

In Bengal, too, population growth was only one of the factors involved, serving to deepen rather than create the structural crisis of the agrarian order. More serious and intractable was the continuing subdivision of landholdings and the chronic burden of indebtedness on the peasants, which left them by the late 1930s in a permanently 'semi-starved condition', without the resources to endure a major crop failure or survive the drying up of credit that invariably accompanied the prospect of a famine in rural India. With no fresh land to occupy and bring under cultivation, peasant holdings were steadily shrinking as the output of rice *per capita* was dwindling. By 1940 one-third of rural households in Bengal were without any land rights and thus without direct and assured access to the produce of the soil. Increasingly Bengal was a society of poor peasants and agricultural labourers, all too dependent on the operations of a volatile and inefficient rice market. Even those who held land generally possessed only miniscule plots. Two-fifths of those with land titles had less than the minimum of two acres of paddy land considered necessary to feed a family of five. Hunger and malnutrition were rife in the province even before the escalating price rises of 1942–43 tipped millions of Bengalis into mass starvation. In Bengal, as in Russia, in Ireland and China, the burden on the peasantry was increasing at a time when there was little or no prospect of radical political change and when alternative economic opportunities were too narrow or too few to offer any realistic prospect of escape. Peasants were certainly not incapable of adaptation or indeed of enduring short-term and seasonal food shortages. And it was not because of 'indolence' or lack of foresight that famine pursued them. But, given their technical and political limitations, peasants could not adapt, compromise and make do indefinitely. With the agrarian order entrenched in a political structure that it was largely beyond the capacity of peasants alone to transform, there was no way in which they could rid themselves of the grim and bitter prospect of famine.

The great escape

But obviously not all peasant societies have been irretrievably trapped in repeated crises of subsistence. Some clearly have escaped. The reasons why and how are inevitably complex – more complex than it is possible to deal with here or necessary for our present purpose to explain. Suffice it to say that the escape from famine has often been possible only within the context of a wider transformation in which a famine-prone peasantry has radically transformed itself from within or been destroyed altogether from without.

England provides a classic and oft-quoted example. Several factors worked together to free England from the famines of the medieval period and from the cycles of high grain prices and want that persisted through into the early nineteenth century. One critical factor was the emergence of a more efficient and productive agriculture. Part of a long-term process, the origins of this development have been traced back as far as the Black Death in the fourteenth century. The resultant weakening of the manorial system, and of the social and economic constraints hitherto associated with it, created opportunities for the more enterprizing farmers to emerge from the mass of the peasantry and, gearing their production to market demand, to prosper into the landholding yeoman farmers and gentry of the sixteenth and seventeenth centuries. Improvements in agricultural technique and practice pioneered in this period were further dispersed and developed during the course of the Agricultural Revolution in the century after 1750. Historians are now more chary than formerly about proclaiming the achievements of this period. It seems not to have revolutionized either techniques or production levels as much as once claimed. None the less, there is evidence enough that through the consolidation of land-holdings (of which the enclosure movement was an important part) and through a combination of better methods of soil management and animal husbandry (such as the greater use of fodder crops and fertilizers and a more scientific approach to animal breeding) substantial increases in arable and livestock production were achieved even before extensive mechanization was introduced. These improvements in agricultural productivity helped to meet (and were further stimulated by) the rising demand from urban centres like London, which alone could boast half a million inhabitants by 1700, and later the new towns and cities spawned by the industrial age. England had long benefited from the ease of access given by its navigable waterways and extensive coastline. Now, improved modes of transportation – the roads and canals of the eighteenth century, the railways of the nineteenth – further contributed to the expansion of a market-oriented agrarian economy. Road and rail facilitated the movement in bulk of foodstuffs from one part of the country to another and dramatically reduced the costs and delays entailed. They virtually eliminated the risk of local shortages becoming serious dearths, and tended to equalize prices across the country as a whole.

It is clear, however, that agriculture in England and Wales alone could not satisfy the needs of a population which nearly trebled between 1750 and 1850 and by the end of the nineteenth century had climbed to almost 33 million people. England's increasing inability to feed itself was made evident during the French Revolutionary and Napoleonic Wars when there were several years of widespread hunger. In 1795 England lurched uncomfortably close to famine. Malthus, in musing three years later upon the perils of confronting an apparently inflexible agriculture with an expanding populace, was reflecting contemporary fears that the country could not find sustenance enough to fill so many hungry mouths. While domestic agriculture was considerably more adaptive than Malthus appreciated, freedom from want and famine was in the end only attainable through the enhanced purchasing power the Industrial Revolution gave to Britain, enabling it to buy an increasing volume of foodstuffs overseas and to exchange manufactured goods for the food and raw materials it needed to sustain its growth. The final repeal of the Corn Laws in 1846 was recognition that the future prosperity of the country was now linked to the availability of cheap and abundant food supplies, from abroad if domestic agriculture could not provide them. By the early twentieth century, sixty years further on, more than 70 per cent of the grain, flour and dairy produce and 40 per cent of the meat consumed in the United Kingdom was imported. The critical readjustment between food supply and population was further eased by the departure of several million migrants, mostly to North America, between the battle of Waterloo and the outbreak of the First World War. Through a unique combination of factors, therefore – the long-term dissolution of the peasantry and its replacement by a class of capitalist farmers, improved agriculture and imported food supplies paid for by the Industrial Revolution – England was able to free itself from the perennial threat of famine for virtually the first time in its history.

Few among the other nations of the world could ever hope to pursue such a course. Never the less, the history of agriculture in the United States of America, in its very different way, shows a complementary process at work. The United States was the main recipient of the millions of peasants, small farmers, and rural labourers who were squeezed out by Europe's changing agrarian economy during the nineteenth century. Their departure enabled capitalist agriculture to establish itself and flourish effectively in many parts of Europe. It meant, too, a weakening of the political resistance as well as the technological obstacle the peasant masses might otherwise have constituted to the agrarian transformation. In abandoning Europe they left the hungry past behind. Many, like the cottiers of Ireland and the crofters of Scotland's highland and islands were driven out by starvation and hunger or expelled through land clearances. A once-populous island like Mull was emptied of two-thirds of its people in the half century between 1821 and 1871 as the potatoes failed and crofting reluctantly made way for sheep-grazing. Many of those who fled from rural Germany, Scandinavia, and latterly from southern and eastern Europe, were likewise deserting minuscule holdings and systems of peasant agriculture that were ceasing to be viable in an age of international markets and agrarian change. Between 1821 and 1914 Europe shed some 44 million people, people it could no longer feed or find room for.

Nearly two-thirds of them went as emigrants to the United States. Peasants, rural labourers and artisans formed the overwhelming proportion. Many were attracted by the prospect of free land held out by the Homestead Act of 1862, and were encouraged by the cheapness of migrant passages to the New World. A passage from Liverpool to New York which had cost £12 in 1816 fell to just over £3 thirty years later, and the great Irish exodus of the late 1840s and 1850s was made possible (albeit in the most wretched shipboard conditions) by passages that cost £5 or less.

Although freedom from want and the prospect of land was a major 'pull factor' for Europe's migrating peasantry, the great exodus did not result in the re-creation of peasant societies in the United States in the image of those left behind in Europe. Many migrants did not, in practice, become farmers, but swelled the urban population, especially in the northeast, becoming construction workers, factory hands, or petty tradesmen instead of resuming a life as peasants and rural labourers. It was a bitter commentary on the tragedy that had forced them from their native land that a large proportion of Irish immigrants turned their backs on agriculture once they arrived in the United States. But even those immigrants who did join the rural sector did not rebuild the old order anew. The institutions and methods of Old World peasant agriculture were not transferable to the New. The emigrants took to farming under conditions that were vastly different from those they had left behind in Europe. Land rights were freely given, without the economic and social constraints of a lingering feudal order. The prairie sod had not been exhausted by a thousand years of peasant toil nor had the great plains of America been divided up into a patchwork of lilliputian plots and narrow strip fields. But, most significantly, American farming in the second half of the nineteenth century was from the outset strongly market-oriented and not geared to household subsistence needs. With abundant land available, low population densities and excellent transport facilities, extensive farming thrived. With more than a quarter of a million miles of railway track criss-crossing the United States by the First World War, farmers could move their grain cheaply, rapidly and in bulk from the prairies of North America to the markets of Europe at prices that further undermined the viability of European peasant farming. The fall in trans-Atlantic freight rates helped, too. Between 1870 and 1900 the cost of transporting grain from the mid-west to Europe fell by three-quarters. Grain exports, valued at $20 million in 1860, touched $150 million before the century was over. In the same period American meat exports multiplied from $15 to $173 million. In addition to satisfying burgeoning demand at home, American agriculture was rapidly emerging as Europe's provisioner as well.

At first held in check by the shortage of labour to sow and reap the abundance of the land, American farmers quickly turned to mechanization. More land could be worked in this way, at lower costs, and without the 'spirit-deadening toil' which had been the hallmark of peasant agriculture in the past. There were, to be sure, areas where American agriculture bore some resemblance to that of the Old World peasantry, as among the land-grubbing poor whites and freed blacks of the post-bellum South. And many pioneers knew to their cost the hardship of drought, severe winters and crop pests. But, in the main, the dynamic nature of American agriculture, its surpluses, its mechanization and market-orientation, prevented natural disasters and times of passing hunger from developing into the recurrent curse of grinding and remorseless famine. The famines of peasant Europe were not for export to the plains and prairies of North America.

This was the great escape; but it was not a path open to all even in the Americas. In parts of Latin America European peasant systems were recreated by the Spanish and Portuguese conquistadores or grafted onto the stock of indigenous cultivators whose heads were already bent in submission to the soil. In Mexico or in the *sertão* of northeastern Brazil peasants were incorporated into a political and social system that had much in common with feudal Europe. Through their poverty and their subordination, through the narrowness of their subsistence and a living wrested from the land, these peasants, too, were exposed to the menace of starvation and famine.

4
Famine's 'Victims'

Images of hunger are among the most powerful and distressing visions of our age. Through the mass media we have become, however dimly, aware of the scenes of Third World hunger from Bihar and Biafra, to Ethiopia, the Sahel and Mozambique. Even in an age jaded by representations of violence and suffering, pictures of starving children, with emaciated limbs, swollen bellies, and great sad eyes, of mothers, dazed with hunger, unable to suckle their frail, thin children, still have the power to shock and disturb us. They point a stark and disquieting contrast with our own unhungry lives.

There can be no denying the real human misery these images represent. And yet, partly because they are images, and thus subject to selection and misinterpretation, we need to treat them with care and to be cautious about any historical conclusion we might draw from them. They project the idea of famine as a blanket phenomenon, reducing all alike to destitution and despair, to a common status as the anonymous 'victims' of disaster. They suggest, perhaps unintentionally, that people struck by famine are powerless and abject, 'pathetic' (as one writer describes them) in their 'submission' to deprivation. They are seen not just to be needy, but also passively dependent upon the benevolence of the West. Such images – and this is a point to which I shall return in the final chapter – present an apparent contrast between western magnanimity and power on the one hand and Third World backwardness and destitution on the other. Famine grants one the honoured role of benefactor and donor while conferring upon the other the permanent and demeaning status of the begging bowl.

It is not, however, only in media imagery that the notion of famine sufferers as 'victims' prevails. Such ideas have been repeatedly endorsed through much of the sociological and medical literature on famine as well. Starvation is seen to be a physiological or pathological state having certain physical characteristics and producing certain social and behavioural responses over which those affected have no real control. One of the most emphatic expressions of this view is to be found in the writings of the sociologist P. A. Sorokin. Influenced by the researches of his fellow Russian, the physiologist I. P. Pavlov, into the 'conditioned reflexes' of the human and animal brain, Sorokin depicted the conduct of the famine-struck in crudely behaviourist terms. The absence or denial of food, he claimed, automatically produced certain 'alimentary reflexes' and caused people to act in a blindly uncontrollable manner. Under the stress of hunger normal rationality and sociability evaporated to be replaced by an 'enormous perversion of behaviour . . . and the disappearance of all conditioned reflexes hindering the satisfaction of hunger'. Starvation made of man 'a naked animal on the naked earth'.

Despite their crudeness, Sorokin's views (or opinions like them) have continued to inform much of the literature on famine in recent times. The Bengal Famine Commission of 1944, which included the nutritional expert W. R. Aykroyd among its members, remarked that in their distress the famine-struck sank to 'sub-human levels' and became 'helpless and hopeless automata guided only by instinctive craving for food'. Elsewhere in their report the authors spoke of the 'mental state' of famine destitutes in Calcutta as a 'pathological condition induced by starvation'. Other medical and official reports on famines since that time have employed similar language to describe the human impact of famine and its physical and psychological consequences – the loss of body weight, the wasting of flesh and muscle, the lowered resistance to infection, the 'listlessness', 'nervous irritability', and 'anti-social activity', which gives way to 'loss of libido', 'apathy', 'immobility' and ultimately death. Here, too, but with the added and impersonal authority of modern medical science, is the idea of the famine-struck as 'victims', rendered powerless, apathetic, irrational by their hunger, needing to be saved and succoured by others.

There is no denying that a cruel and tragic process of mental and bodily deterioration takes place as a result of prolonged hunger and the concomitant physical and social effects of famine. But there is a danger, in representing human experience exclusively in these terms, of overlooking the ways in which the famine-struck actively resist the onset of hunger and destitution, and, for as long as they are able to do so, do not passively accept the status of 'victims' the outside world so readily assigns them. To see starvation *only* as a pathological or physiological state is to deny to famine sufferers the capacity for self-help, for moral indignation and rational protest. It is to depoliticize and dehumanize them by reducing their behaviour to the unthinking reflexes of Pavlov's salivating dogs.

Famine responses

That the nature of famine's immediate causes varied greatly from one context to another was itself important in shaping local responses. A flood, for instance, or a tidal wave might strike virtually without warning and leave little or no time for any anticipatory or evasive action. On such occasions adaptation came after the event. But in the case of drought, undoubtedly one of the commonest factors in triggering famine, or of the cumulative effect of unseasonal frosts and excessive rain, or the blight that spoiled Ireland's potato crop three years in succession – all these tragedies took weeks, months, even years to evolve, and were met by an unfolding sequence of human responses.

To officials and townsmen a famine only began once its existence could no longer be denied, when it announced itself by irrefutable signs – withered crops, soaring food prices and shortages in the market-place, the pinched faces and matchstick limbs of the rural poor who began to invade the towns to beg in the streets or from door to door. But for villagers the realization that famine was on its way came much sooner.

The fickleness of nature was an indisputable fact in peasant life, and found ample reflection in peasant lore and religion. Many of the principal festivals and ceremonies of the village calendar were either to thank the gods for their harvest bounty or to plead for their benevolent intercession in the season to follow. The hymns of our harvest-time still echo such peasant sensibilities. In many agrarian societies the first ploughing or first reaping of the year was an occasion rich with ceremony and pregnant with meaning. Cultivators in Malabar on the southwest coast of India, to choose but one instance, used to sacrifice a fowl to the god Mallan before starting the annual sowing. If the crop then failed or was ruined by blight and pests they knew that the rituals had not been properly performed and that the god had been displeased. The possibility that the rains might not fall or the crops might fail was an ever-present concern.

Aware of each change in the weather, the state of the crops and the environment generally, peasant farmers watched anxiously for telltale signs and clues to guide them – when to plough or reap, when to expect storms or prepare for drought. 'If it rains in Tulam [October-November]', ran one south Indian prognostic, 'the crops will be well'. 'If there is rain in Arudra [late June to early August]', declared another reassuringly, 'there will be no scarcity'. Peasants read omens into the flight of birds, into the sudden appearance of one insect species or the rain dance of another, saw meteorological significance in the wilting of one plant or the abnormal abundance of its neighbour. 'Tamarinds in a good season', advised one Telugu saying, 'mangoes in a bad', while another warned that 'if the *kalivi* [tree] fruits well, famine will appear'. There were, in truth, so many such sayings, some flagrantly contradicting others, that little credence might be attached to them – at least by outsiders. But peasants usually read the weather signs well enough to know far in advance that a season of hardship was fast approaching. If by a certain date (often a particular feast day or festival) the rains had not fallen or, having arrived, had not ceased, then alarm grew apace.

One of the first responses was likely to be an intensification of ritual. Since the heavens were thought to control the elements, it was logical to appeal for a god's help, or to seek to atone for the sins that had manifestly provoked divine displeasure. Prayers offered up in churches, temples and mosques, were supplemented by special rituals and ceremonies in the streets, fields and public places. In England during the interminably rainy summer of 1315,

> the archbishop of Canterbury ordered the clergy to perform solemn, barefoot processions bearing the Sacrament and relics, accompanied by the ringing of bells, chanting of the litany, and the celebration of mass. This was in the hope of encouraging the people to atone for their sins and appease the wrath of God by prayer, alms-giving, and other charitable works.[1]

Deities, saints, even plants and animals particularly associated with rain were invoked in times of drought. In some parts of India villagers tied a frog to a tree, so that its pitiful cries would draw the attention of the rain god Varuna who seemed deaf to human entreaties. In Bellary, one of the most famine-prone districts of southern India, a procession of women and children wound through a village bearing a frog tied to a winnowing fan from door to door, singing:

> Mother frog should have her bath.
> The tanks are full [They were not, but needed to be]
> Give water, oh Rain God

At the entrance to each household a woman sprinkled the unfortunate frog with water. In some parts of India, women held mock ploughing

1. Ian Kershaw, 'The Great Famine and Agrarian Crisis in England 1315-1322', *Past and Present*, 1973, p. 7.

ceremonies in the fields at night to shame the gods into releasing their showers, or danced wild dances, their hair tossed loose and swirling about their heads, in imitation of the frenzy of a tropical downpour, to draw down rain from the sullen skies. When the rains failed in Malawi (Nyasaland) in December 1948, peasants prayed to their ancestors for help:

> Our dead fathers
> What have we done?
> Forgive us, please, please!
> Have mercy on us,
> Do you want us to die?
> Please, send us rain.[2]

Religious rituals and ceremonies provided a culturally acceptable reason why the rains had not come or fell in such destructive excess: it was due to the sins and omissions of men, the anger or negligence of the gods. In rendering calamity intelligible, religion also provided guidelines for seemingly appropriate remedial action. It was important, too, that these were public rites, involving some degree of community participation. The whole village (or perhaps, as in India, its womenfolk) was expected to participate (for only then would it be effective in moving the heavens) and to help avert a crisis that might threaten them all with misery and loss.

When rituals failed to bring relief, more divisive or desperate responses followed. Scapegoats were sought out and punished for 'holding the rain' for their own ends. When the monsoons failed in Gujarat in western India the Bhil *adivasis* or tribals suspected Bania traders of stopping the rain deliberately so as to profit from the resultant dearth and high prices. To break this spell the Bhils forced a Bania to hold a water pot on his head at which they fired arrows until the pot broke and released the rains. In Malawi in 1949 suspicion similarly fell on old men with grey hair or bald heads, and on brickmakers (for who else stood to gain by the absence of rain?). Elsewhere old women were accused of being witches, malevolently driving away the rain clouds with their sorcery. In nineteenth-century Brazil (much as in medieval Europe) the physical suffering and spiritual anguish brought on by famine and pestilence bred religious fanaticism of the kind powerfully evoked in Mario Vargas Llosa's novel, *The War of the End of the World*. Just as Europe had its Flagellants, so, as the terrible drought of 1877–78 moved towards its

2. Megan Vaughan, *The Story of an African Famine*, p. 30.

brutal climax, the peasants of the Brazilian backlands formed 'penitential processions, cutting themselves with knives, carrying heavy stones on their heads, and crying and beating their breasts'.

In some instances the persistence of drought even caused doubts about the gods of the established pantheon. During the famines of the late 1870s in India and China, western missionaries won some converts by pointing to the apparent failure of local deities to protect even their most ardent worshippers from want and by claiming that theirs alone was a merciful and benevolent god. The inducement to switch faiths was backed by a powerful material incentive, as the contemptuous term 'rice Christians' applied to the converts by followers of the old faith clearly indicated. Historically, however, examples of a famine-induced loss or transference of faith must have been rare if only because drought, famine and other afflictions were widely interpreted as divine punishments that needed to be atoned for or endured, and from which there could be no easy escape.

The cultural context of famine, of course, varied enormously. Some religions, sects, and societies, took a more resigned view of the impending crisis than others. Some placed great faith in divine will and believed it blasphemous even to question god's purposes and intentions. But peasants were pragmatists, too, and, for as long as they were able, they coupled their prayers and entreaties with practical agricultural measures. The planting of a crop, if not already begun, would be delayed until there was no longer hope of sufficient rain or time to bring it to harvest. Other crop varieties, with a lower yield perhaps, but a shorter growing season or a lower water requirement, might be substituted. Sometimes two or three sowings of the same crop were attempted before the peasant gave up or ran out of seed. Part of the holding might be abandoned, so that effort could be concentrated on a better watered or more fertile spot, such as the bed of a stream that still retained moisture after the rest of the land had turned to dust. But there were, of course, severe limits to such adaptability. A poor peasant was unlikely to have kept aside (or been able to borrow) enough seed grain for more than one or two sowings, and purchasing fresh seed was almost certainly beyond his means and credit in an unpromising season. Such were the bitter dilemmas of hunger that a household might decide to consume its seed grain rather than to sow it in the waterless soil or try to hold on to it until the next season's rains.

Accustomed to the economies of consumption forced upon them by the annual 'hungry gap', peasants responded to advancing famine by reducing the amount of food consumed at each meal and by spacing

meals out over longer and longer intervals. Those who bought their
food in the market might switch to cheaper, less favoured foods. One
sign of incipient famine in India was the shift from costly rice to
cheaper, but less prestigious, millets. To eke out food supplies,
peasants began to add other ingredients, some familiar from the
seasonal times of hunger, others indicative of the increasingly
desperate attempt to stave off gnawing hunger. In Russia in the late
nineteenth century peasants made 'famine bread', mixing with a little
rye a plant known as 'goosefoot' that grew wild in the fields even when
sown crops failed. It gave the bread a yellowish colour and a bitter
taste. Its continued use brought on headaches, vomiting and diarrhoea.

As the food crisis deepened the rural poor began to range further
beyond foods to which they had some seasonal recourse to those whose
very use bore famine's stamp. Abandoning their barren or blighted
fields, they resorted to the methods of their foraging ancestors, but
from a countryside now ill-stocked to satisfy the needs of such hungry
multitudes. In the Sahelian drought of 1931, peasants in Niger cut
down palm trees to roast and eat the pith as 'palm cabbage'. That and
the eating of lily roots was one of the clearest signs of impending
famine. By the middle months of 1877 the poor of northeastern Brazil
were driven by hunger to eat seeds of the *mucuman* plant, which
caused dropsy and death, and chew the roots of the *pāo de moco*, a
shrub whose toxic tubers brought on blindness only hours after being
eaten. In Ireland's 'Great Hunger', peasants searched the fields and
the seashore for anything – nettles, berries, fungi, seaweed, frogs and
rats – that could be eaten. Cattle were bled for the nourishment of
their blood. Charlock, a weed which grew wild in the fields, became
immortalized in folk memory as the food of the famine poor.

India's famine-struck, too, foraged for whatever food they could
find, moving from familiar plants to 'things not ordinarily eaten', such
as snails. They picked up individual grains of rice or millet that had
fallen from passing carts or laboriously extracted them from animal
dung and anthills. A day's search yielded a pitiful handful of barely
digestible food. In China peasants ate grass, bark, even earth to try to
assuage their incessant hunger. Sometimes the effects of drought
brought the poorest of the rural population a few temporary windfalls.
As the drought worsened in the Brazilian *sertāo* in 1876 herdsmen
began to kill the cattle they could no longer feed for the price of their
hides and tallow. For a brief while the poor could beg at the slaugh-
terhouse gates for scraps of meat and bones. When, in the same
terrible year of drought and hunger, cattle began to perish in their
thousands in South India, caste Hindus would not touch their flesh;

but their untouchable labourers, who did not share such scruples, stayed alive by eating the carcases of the dead animals. But, unless there was a dramatic turnabout in the season or outside relief arrived, such expedients were shortlived and soon exhausted.

In a bid to stay alive and buy food, peasants sold the few assets they had. Houses were stripped of their furniture, doors and window-frames. Thatch was torn from roofs to feed the remaining cattle. Women sold their cooking pots and jewelry, which, in a glutted market, brought far less than their worth. Everything in a famine fell in price (even, one might say, the value placed on life itself) – except the price of food which continued to soar where it was even available at all. Farm implements and draught animals were sold, further jeopardizing prospects for agricultural recovery after the famine. Peasants might try to borrow money, too, especially in societies like that of nineteenth- and early twentieth-century India where credit was needed even in normal years for peasants to buy seed grain and enough food to last them till the harvest. But moneylenders were loath to give credit in years when the monsoon seemed destined to fail and there would be no harvest to lay claim to. Peasants might be forced by hunger and want to sell off part or even all of their land. Land sales, like 'famine foods' or migration, were one of the unmistakable signs of acute and deepening crisis. In Bengal during the 1943–44 famine the volume of land sales rose sharply as small peasant proprietors sold out to more prosperous men. A quarter of a million households parted with their paddyland; 660,000 more sold part of their holdings. Considering the importance of land to a peasant's livelihood and identity, this was a mark of sheer desperation. Losing land as a result of famine was one of the ways in which property-holding peasants sank into the residual class of landless labourers. The sale brought short-term relief from starvation; but many peasants had no land to sell in the first place, or they clung to the little they had as a last vestige of pride and as security against future hunger.

The 'moral economy' of the poor

It has been argued that in societies where peasants habitually lived in the shadow of hunger they developed, or were the beneficiaries of, social and cultural practices which ensured that even the poorest of villagers would not starve to death. In Southeast Asia, for example, James C. Scott has suggested that there traditionally existed ideas of 'shared poverty' and 'mutual assistance' that operated through the pressure of social values to effect a partial redistribution of resources between village households. Those who had food shared part of it with destitute kinsmen and needy neighbours. Such practices and conventions guaranteed that the poor had at least enough food to stay alive. Similar networks of mutual assistance have been identified in many other peasant societies, too. B. M. Bhatia in his study of *Famines in India* claimed that in pre-colonial times caste ties and the Hindu joint family system saved the poor and infirm from absolute want. 'India', he claimed, 'had no Poor Law because the need for one under the medieval system of social organization was never felt.' With the advent of colonialism, however, the old social order decayed. The new social classes that emerged under British rule declined to recognize such obligations, and so the 'fountains of private charity dried up'. In Scotland, it has been said, the clan system traditionally gave support to the poor and aged and only once this broke down was there a need for public charity and parish poorhouses.

More complex social and economic relations are said to have arisen, too, out of the perennial quest for protection against hunger. In village India poorer peasants and landless labourers attached themselves to wealthy rural patrons, readily accepting positions as dependent clients and tenants in the belief that in times of dearth they would be rewarded with at least a minimum subsistence. To the patron accrued social prestige, a potentially useful following, and command over a reliable labour force or a substantial share of the harvest produced by tenants and sharecroppers. To the client such arrangements gave protection. The risks of cultivation were shared, and there was the hope of freedom from absolute want. Hunger, as a perennial threat to peasant subsistence and survival, has thus come to be seen as a primary motivating force in the creation of elaborate village hierarchies and the maintenance of reciprocal patron-client relations.

These claims, however, raise a host of questions about the nature of rural societies in pre-industrial or pre-colonial times. For example, were clan and caste heads, landlords and rich peasants, or even wealthier relatives, really willing to surrender part of their income to keep poor clansmen, kinsfolk and villagers alive? Did they perhaps only pay lip-service to ideas of 'shared poverty' and a 'moral economy' the better to conceal their rank acquisitiveness? Did they only respond to the demands of a supposedly 'moral' economy when the threat of physical violence, pillage, or the loss of their labour force left them with no practical alternative? And, most centrally to our concerns, what happened when the village was faced not just by an occasional poor crop and individual hunger but by acute and protracted food shortages?

If, as the 'moral economy' argument suggests, the threat of hunger helped to maintain economic and social relations in normal times and erect a hierarchical social order which even the poorest had an interest in upholding, then the reality of famine threatened moral and social collapse. Up to a point, while the outcome of the season was still uncertain, landlords and patrons made some provision for labourers and poor peasants. But once the signs of famine were clearly evident, many a landholder responded by dismissing or 'casting off' his field hands. Without work in the fields, and perhaps with only limited reserves of his own to see him through a crisis, a landholder seldom recognized a binding obligation to feed the landless. Some labourers protested; others drifted to the towns in search of food. As the crisis deepened, however, other sections of the agrarian society became affected by the shrinking of the landholder's patronage and support. The fishermen and barbers Amartya Sen discusses in connection with the Bengal famine of 1943–44, the weavers, who appear in the earliest reports of famine distress in nineteeth-century India, even poor priests dependent upon village patronage, found that their services or their products, too, were no longer required. Their 'entitlements' simply evaporated. Their incomes dwindled as prices rose and food grew scarce. As Sen points out, it was not necessarily the actual non-availability of food that was important: these were the 'work' or 'price' famines of the Indian famine reports. The dependent labourers and artisans found themselves without either the employment with which to earn money (or its grain equivalents) or access to the cash and credit needed to obtain food from the local bazaars. Nor was this discarding of labourers and other rural dependants solely an Indian or Asian phenomenon. It occurred in many another famine-stricken societies as well. In 1602, during Muscovy's 'Time of Troubles', Russian landlords who were 'unable or unwilling to feed their villeins freed or drove them out'. 'Ruined and starving', poor peasants 'were forced to flee or to resist'. Here, too, customary ties and obligations proved unable to withstand the pressures of the famine situation.

The tendency to dismiss unwanted dependants may have been all the more pronounced in situations where the state (rather than the landlords) had come to be seen as responsible for providing relief, or where 'traditional' values (if ever operative to the extent writers like Bhatia claim) had been eroded by the growth of a market economy in food and land. It was noted, for example, in India during the famines of the late nineteenth century that many of the leading landholders or *zamindars* had neither the funds nor the inclination to feed the tenants on their estates. They left it instead to the colonial administration or to urban-based relief committees and religious charities to perform this function. But there were, of course, exceptions. In the Orissa famine of 1866 the older *zamindars*, who were the hereditary chiefs of the people, showed far more willingness to help their *raiyats* than those landholders who had but recently purchased estates in the area and who were mostly outsiders and absentees.

But the rural poor seldom accepted being cast off in this manner without protest. One of the limitations of Sen's 'entitlement' thesis is that it takes too narrow and legalistic a view of what people believed themselves entitled to. In practice, in many a famine situation relations of dependence and responsibility between those who possessed food and those who needed food were bitterly contested. Rather than 'apathy' and 'inertia', instead of meekly accepting the role of 'victims', poor peasants and labourers frequently responded forcefully and vociferously to what they saw as the callous neglect or disregard of their right to eat and stay alive. Groups of labourers and tenants petitioned their landlords and patrons demanding to be fed; they carried their protests to any official who would hear them. Sometimes, more through the threat of violence than the force of argument, they succeeded in winning a few concessions – a gift of grain, perhaps, or the promise that their needs would be duly attended to. But if they were ignored, their sense of what was right and just might drive them to break open the grain stores of wealthier villagers, loot market stalls and warehouses, and attack carts and barges that were transporting food to market or carrying it away elsewhere for sale.

It is at such moments of mounting tension, anger and fear that the idea of the poor having a right to food was most forcefully evinced. The unmistakable signs of 'moral' protest, backed by popular consensus and appeals to longstanding and legitimate rights, encourages us to treat with caution those biomedical and behaviourist interpretations of hunger which explain away such episodes as merely expressions of 'nervous excitement' and 'irritability' or a form of 'anti-social behaviour' akin to that observable among starving laboratory rats. As E. P. Thompson remarks in his account of the 'Moral Economy of the English Crowd in the Eighteenth Century', dearth came as a 'profound psychic shock'. When it was 'accompanied by the knowledge of inequalities, and the suspicion of manipulated scarcity, shock passe[d] into fury'. In many such market-place incidences, well-documented for eighteenth-century France as well as England, the populace fixed

and paid what it believed to be the rightful or customary price for the
food seized. Sometimes the purpose was more to make a protest than
to satisfy the 'instincts' of hunger by simply grabbing food for
consumption. Goods were tipped over, spoiled, or carried off only to
be discarded in a ditch or alleyway shortly afterwards.

These incidents in the countryside and market towns opened up, or
revealed more starkly than in prosperous times, the conflicts between
the growers and marketers of grain and those who consumed it. A
powerful sense of deprivation and fear of imminent hunger gained
further potency from rumours that speculators and wealthy landholders and traders had hoarded vast quantities of food for their own
profit and consumption. As Slicher van Bath rather condescendingly
noted:[3]

> It is especially bewildering to the people that times of scarcity are just
> when the traffic in grain increases, because the enhanced prices make it
> possible to cover the cost of transporting it from much greater distances.
> Never are more carts and shiploads of grain to be seen than in times of
> need. The famished people draw the conclusion that there is plenty of
> corn to be had, and that only the manipulations of speculators and the
> inefficiency of the government are driving prices beyond their reach.

But the indignation of the poor arose from more than some simple-
minded inability to understand the operation of market forces. Not
only were prices high and food beyond their power to afford, but
others were seen to be profiting by their hardship and misfortune. For
those landholders who managed to produce even a partial crop in a bad
year or for those merchants who could move grain unmolested to
where prices ruled highest, there were exceptional profits to be had.
So were there for traders who bought the peasant's land or oxen at
knock-down prices or who grew rich selling the skins of slaughtered
sheep and cattle. Resentment at the activities of speculators and
traders informed present anger but also stored up resentment for the
future as well. Famine was thus more likely to accentuate social
division rather than to play the greater leveller, though the longer it
persisted the more likely it was to have a depressing effect on the
society and economy at large. In a prolonged drought, like those of the
late 1870s in India and China, even richer peasants, small landholders
and moneylenders began to succumb, selling up their assets and
themselves feeling the pinch of hunger.

3. *Agrarian History of Western Europe*, p. 120.

Yet, for all the social conflicts and economic tensions they revealed, food riots and looting need to be understood for the limited phenomenon they generally were. Except when, as in France in 1789, popular distress chimed with elite dissent and state ineptitude, such eruptions seldom proved overtures to revolution. Dearth worried and strained the social order, and yet, paradoxically, it could also contribute to its long-term durability. The protestors were anxious to draw attention to their plight and force landholders, traders and officials to act in accordance with what they saw to be their legitimate rights and pressing needs. That did not necessarily make them intent upon society's overthrow and destruction. Swift and effective intervention by the elite, even the token gestures and partial concessions that more commonly followed and served as little more than temporary palliatives, might still the threat of violence. Meeting the immediate needs of the poor might even win their gratitude, while insuring property, order and authority against serious harm. This was an outcome that the magistrates and gentry of Manchu China were as anxious to achieve as their counterparts in Hanoverian England. Besides, food riots could not last indefinitely. They died away once either provision was made for the basic needs of the poor or, more commonly perhaps, the situation deteriorated still further. When there was no grain to be had whether by looting or by purchase, once troops stood guard over market-places and granaries, the hungry were obliged to look for other solutions.

One common alternative lay in recourse to what officialdom and the propertied elites saw as crime, and, like food riots and looting, this was a characteristic and almost universal feature of the famine response. Here, too, Sen's 'entitlements' thesis, with its emphasis upon purely legal entitlements, appears deficient. The appropriations of the poor in famine situations could themselves be significant in helping to stave off hunger: they might also be the necessary spur to private charity and state relief. The poor did not accept the denial of their entitlements without contest. Famine crime assumed many forms. In some instances it was simply an intensification of the banditry, sheep-stealing, and petty theft to which many poor peasants resorted in barren lands and at hungry times of year. Sometimes it was barely distinguishable from looting. In Orissa in 1866 gangs of hungry villagers, ten to twenty in number, broke into the houses of wealthier men and carried off as much grain as they could carry. Some sat down to feast on unfinished meals before departing with the rest of their spoils. The raiders seldom harmed the householders and made little attempt to conceal their identity. When arrested they freely confessed to what they had done and even voluntarily surrendered what they had taken. An element of protest and moral indignation lingered on through actions such as these.

But as society fractured and split under famine's pressure, so collective action and protest gave way to more individualistic acts of violence and theft. Grain was filched from fields, jewelry snatched from those foolish enough to parade it. Strangers were murdered for a few rupees or a crust of bread. Worse still, families turned against each other. Husbands and wives killed one another or murdered their offspring rather than have to share a last spoonful of gruel. From whatever cause and by whatever means, crimes against property and persons soared. Many of them, reports attest, were committed by people 'not ordinarily criminal', and increasingly, as protest waned or became ineffectual, it was a case of the poor robbing the poor. Even in Ireland, where wholesale looting and the organized robbery of grain stores were, it seems, rare, food stealing, mainly at night from the fields of those who still had a few potatoes or turnips, was reportedly common; and crimes against property increased threefold in 1846 over the previous (pre-famine) year. Although the Bengal Commission of 1944 noted a surprising absence of violence and looting, in general in India years of dearth were years of exceptional levels of crime. The Orissa famine of 1866 and the Madras famine of 1876–8 produced the highest rates of agrarian crime reported in those provinces over the entire period from the 1850s to the Second World War.

Women in famine

The burden of famine fell, and in many Third World societies continues to fall, with exceptional severity upon women. One reason for this is that in many parts of the world women traditionally have either been the main agricultural producers or constituted a substantial part of the agrarian work force. In sub-Saharan Africa, in particular, women performed most of the work of cultivation. Under a system of shifting cultivation, men might carry out the initial labour of felling and burning the forest, but thereafter the work of planting, hoeing and harvesting would be left almost exclusively to the women. The sexual disparity of agrarian labour in Africa was further accentuated, Ester Boserup has pointed out, by the advent of male-oriented colonial regimes which had no sympathy for, or practical interest in, systems of farming in which women played a leading role. Education and new employment opportunities were directed towards the men, who took up work in the mines, on estates and in the cities, often at considerable distances from their home villages, thus further weakening their commitment to subsistence agriculture. Even in systems of plough cultivation, such as were to be found in many areas of monsoon Asia, where men exercised a dominant role, female labour was of vital importance to agricultural production and to family food and income generation. Such skilled but arduous work as transplanting the young rice-plants was commonly done by women, working in rows, up to their calves in the mud of flooded paddy-fields. The onset of famine conditions thus hit women directly. The food that they normally produced through their labour was abruptly lost to themselves and to their families, and when field labourers were dismissed or left without employment they, too, lost their income in cash or in kind.

In addition to food provisioning, women had primary responsibility for domestic tasks that were also adversely affected by drought and famine. For instance, when wells dried up and streams ran dry, women, as the principal drawers of water, were forced to search further and further afield for water to drink and cook with. Sustained drought similarly exacerbated the women's task of fuel collection, already a laborious one in areas where generations of intensive peasant agriculture had stripped the landscape almost bare of trees.

Women, like men, could attempt to keep themselves and their dependants alive by pursuing various adaptive strategies. But the strategies open to women were often more limited or even more demeaning and self-abasing than those undertaken by men, and some involved a permanent loss of such limited status and independence as women had formerly enjoyed. In pastoralist and semi-nomadic communities, women and children generally migrated with the men in search of water and pasturage for their animals. But in village-based peasant communities the physical mobility of women was considerably more constricted. When the men departed in search of work and food – to relatives, to the cities, even abroad – the women generally remained behind, with the children and aged relatives as well as themselves to look after. In Bengal in 1943 women, especially those without male relatives to support them, took up the lowly and laborious work of paddy-husking. In coastal Orissa in 1866, as in many African famines, when the men departed or died, women and children searched the fields for roots, edible greens and other 'famine foods'. In India peasant men of 'respectable' castes commonly regarded 'coolie' work on government relief works as too demeaning for them, even in times of extreme dearth. Instead, it was often the women of the household, taking their children with them and setting aside their own unfamiliarity with such work (and, in many instances, overcoming their customary seclusion in the home and village as well), who turned up to excavate earth from reservoirs, break road metal and build embankments.

Before the onset of famine itself, while dearth and hunger still only threatened, women had a significant role in anticipatory responses. In the ritual context, as indicated earlier, women were prominent in rain-making rites – indeed, in many cases the participants were exclusively women or consisted of women and children alone. There appear to be several reasons for this. Women were identified in peasant society with the fertility of the fields as well as the fecundity of the family, and thus their involvement was of great symbolic significance. Despite the male monopoly of religious office, in this exceptional context, where men's rituals and devotions had clearly failed, women's prayers and entreaties were credited with superior power to shame the gods or to move the heavens to pity and so release the necessary showers.

But women also had a practical responsibility for food provisioning and their role in rain-making rituals perhaps also tacitly acknowledged this. As purchasers of food in the markets and bazaars women sometimes took part in demonstrations over high prices or joined with men in deputations to traders and officials. In some instances, certainly in Europe, women participated in food riots and the seizure of grain from barges, carts and warehouses. As the preparers of domestic food and as wives and mothers, women bore responsibility for basic decisions about food provisioning and food sharing, and it was through their ingenuity that dwindling supplies were eked out for as long as possible by reducing the amount consumed at each meal or mixing in surrogate foodstuffs.

Several recent studies of food shortages and famine in Africa have shown how women engaged in food sharing activities, seeking gifts and loans from their family and friends, or helping poorer, especially female, relatives through the hardships caused by worsening food shortages. In Malawi in 1949, according to Megan Vaughan, many wives were deserted when their menfolk departed for other parts of the territory. For a while other women helped out, but in time, when there was no food left to share communally, these networks of mutual support began to break down. The few people who had food now 'ate alone, in the dark and secretly'. Women who had husbands to send them money or bring them grain fared best; those without male providers suffered most acutely from the drying up of communal and family support.

The burden of famine also fell heavily upon women because of their customary low status in male-dominated societies. In this sense, famine can be seen as causing an intensification of a system of gender subordination and exploitation that was ever-present in daily life. In his study of the famine of 1943–44, *Prosperity and Misery in Modern Bengal*, Paul Greenough argues that the patriarchal values of Bengali Hindu society required priority to be given to the feeding of the male members of the household so as to ensure the continuance of the male line. The counterpart of this was a cultural expectation that women would sacrifice their food and ultimately their lives to enable their husbands and sons to survive. The cultural imperative Greenough describes is, to some degree, evident enough not just in Bengal but in many parts of South Asia. Even in normal times men are fed first in peasant households. Women eat after the men, receiving a smaller and poorer share of food. When food is short (or when disease strikes) female children tend to be neglected and food resources and medical attention are concentrated on male offspring. In this way a barely covert form of female infanticide has often been practised. But Greenough takes this principle of gender discrimination a stage further and contends that during the Bengal famine food was deliberately withheld from women and given to men. Women were neglected and starved, abandoned by their men, sent off to search for their own food, or sold into prostitution – 'victimized', in short, in the interests of male survival.

There is certainly evidence from many famine histories (and not just those for Bengal or even India) to show that part of the burden of hunger and suffering was transferred in this way. It should be noted, however, that in practice women did not simply accept the 'victim' status men – or the male-ordered cultural system – imposed upon them. Although clearly a very problematic source in themselves, recorded rates of mortality during famines in India and elsewhere do not show that women died in substantially greater numbers than men. In Bengal in 1943 male deaths as usual outnumbered female deaths, and the Famine Commission took the view that, except in Calcutta, where a large number of destitute women congregated, male mortality probably did in actuality exceed that of females. From her study of the demographic evidence for western India in the second half of the nineteenth century, Michelle McAlpin, like a number of other writers, concluded that 'females may be better able than males to withstand the trials of a period of famine' and that it was the young and old of both sexes who suffered the greatest loss through starvation and disease. It might be concluded from this that perhaps women were not as generally abandoned as Greenough's cultural hypothesis suggests or that men suffered no less severely from sickness, hunger and exhaustion. Arguably, too, women succeeded in keeping themselves alive by recourse to the kind of adaptive strategies discussed above, and thus, in effect, contested their 'victim' status.

It is indisputable, however, that famine imposed enormous physical and emotional suffering upon women and that both gender discrimination and the multiplicity of female roles contributed to this, as the anguish and ordeals of the central character in Satyajit Ray's film *Distant Thunder* eloquently testify. As mothers, often deserted by their husbands, women had to endure the hunger and suffering of their children without having any means to help them. Megan Vaughan, in describing the particular distress of women who lost their children (and also temporarily their power to conceive) during the Malawi famine of 1949, gives the song of a young woman left without a child of her own:

> I am the nurse of the sun
> I am nursing the sun
> While my friends are nursing babies[4]

Such was the agony of some women that they strangled or drowned their children because they could no longer feed them or endure the endless crying and pleading for food. Others internalized their grief, ending their own lives rather than continue to suffer the torment of hunger or watch it agonizingly end the lives of others. Many marital relationships were strained to breaking point and there were 'tacit divorces' as men and women took separate paths in their search for food and security. The year 1949 was long remembered in Malawi (and recalled through the women's maize-pounding songs) as a time of broken marriages and divorces:

> We have suffered this year
> Our men are divorcing us.
> Oh, what shall we do with this hunger?

Abandonment and hunger drove women into prostitution and slavery. Without men to provide food and security for them, and unable even, in a male-oriented society, to maintain their social identity, they lost the capacity to support themselves and could not

4. *The Story of an African Famine*, p. 35.

live alone. They were sold by others, or, for the price of their maize or rice, sold themselves, as prostitutes or slaves. In this again, the abnormality of famine – for all that it represented the disintegration of the conventional moral and social order – was not a complete departure from the everyday world. The sexual exploitation of peasant women by landholders, moneylenders and other males in a position of authority over them was not uncommon at any time – indeed it was one of the most emphatic reminders of the physical and social surbordination of the peasant and labouring classes. Famine, then, was its intensifier.

In Malawi in 1949 the descent into prostitution was apparently covert and temporary. But in many other cases, as in the major famines in India and China, it represented initiation into a permanent life of prostitution. Female orphans escaped the Orissa famine of 1866 only to end up in the brothels of Cuttack and Calcutta. In China one of the commonest responses to famine, recorded over many centuries, was the sale of children. Boys as well as girls were disposed of in this way by parents who could no longer feed them or who had come to see them, in their desperation, as their only means of obtaining food. But some boys bought in this way attained the status of adopted sons and heirs while girls faced only a lifetime of servitude and concubinage. The devaluing of female life that occurred in famine often further favoured male power and ascendancy. As Meredeth Turshen observes of East Africa, through famine a wealthy man could acquire many wives (and thereby increase his social status and dependent work force) for in famine times parents were willing to part with their daughters for the little dowry they would bring.

Migration

One of the most important survival strategies to which famine-struck populations had recourse was migration. It was as common a response to food shortages in medieval Europe as it was to the famines of nineteenth- and twentieth-century India, China and Africa. But this characteristic response has often been seen in a purely negative light. British officials in late nineteenth-century India spoke disparagingly of famine 'wandering' and stressed its 'irrational' nature, much as some modern writers see in it evidence of listlessness and disorientation, a behavioural response brought on by the physical effects of prolonged hunger. Certainly, the tendency of populations to migrate in times of hunger has often accentuated famine's hardship and misery – for the migrants themselves, worn out still more by their wanderings, but also for the people of adjacent areas to whom they carried their epidemic diseases and extended their ravening hunger. It was partly for such reasons that British famine relief measures by the close of the nineteenth century aimed to prevent migration and encourage those affected by drought and hunger to stay close to their villages and fields. But from an historical perspective famine migration, in its various forms, constituted an important survival strategy and contributed to famine's most significant long-term effects.

Much famine migration was short-term and relatively local. Unable to find work and food for themselves or fodder and water for their animals, peasants migrated temporarily to more favoured places. During the Indian famines of the late nineteenth century there were many such mass migrations away from barren, drought-baked plains to forested uplands like the Nilgiris, the 'blue mountains' of the south, or to the canal-irrigated tracts along the Ganges in the north, where food and fodder could still be found. In the famine of 1860–61 in the Northwestern Provinces, an estimated half a million people moved from their homes in this way. In the South Indian famine of 1876–78 peasants fled from the famine-stricken states of Mysore and Hyderabad into British India in search of relief, while those from the parched interior districts of the Madras Presidency made for the well-watered paddylands and rich temple towns of Thanjavur district in the Kaveri delta. In the Bengal famine of 1943–44 the poor deserted the countryside – many travelling ticketless on the trains – for Calcutta, where they had good reason to believe food could be found. By the second half of 1943 between 80,000 and 150,000 destitutes had crowded into the city. About 300,000 more headed for the green hills of Assam. This pattern of temporary migration was not a purely Indian phenomenon. In similar fashion in Malawi in 1949 men left the plains around Blantyre for upland areas where they had relatives from whom they could beg or borrow food. In both societies, as already noted, migration was more of a male than a female response: the women were left at home to look after the children or drifted to local relief works. But whole families sometimes moved to the towns or in search of fodder and pasturage for their cattle. Women also arrived alone in the cities to beg or scavenge for food.

Once famine migration began it rapidly became a flood. When in northeastern Brazil there was still no sign of an end to the months of remorseless drought by March 1878 the starving peasants finally abandoned hope of the long-awaited rains.

> Then, as by one impulse, a wild panic caught them. Four hundred thousand, they deserted the *sertão* and rushed down to the coast. Oh! it was terrible that mad flight. Over all the roads there came streams of fugitives, men and women and little children, naked, lean, famine-weak, dragging wearily across the plains, staining the rocky mountain-paths with their bleeding feet, begging, praying at every house for a morsel of food.[5]

By April the interior of the state of Ceará was an empty wilderness while as many as 100,000 famine refugees crowded into the town of Fortaleza, normally home to only 25,000 people. Thousands died in this 'metropolis of hunger' from starvation and disease before food and medical relief could reach them. The flight from the *secas* (droughts), so dramatically and tragically observed in 1878, was repeated on a lesser scale in subsequent years of hardship – in 1915, 1930–32, 1942 and 1958. But temporary flight also turned into permanent migration as peasants from the northeast abandoned their homes to become settlers and rubber-gatherers in the jungles of Amazonia in the late nineteenth century just as later they provided labour for the factories of São Paulo and the building of Brasilia. Famine in Brazil, as elsewhere, has been one of the most irresistible goads to human migration.

During the nineteenth century famine was one of the impelling forces, too, behind the Indian diaspora. Indian indentured labour provided the British with a workforce to replace the prohibited African slave trade and to work on sugar plantations and estates as far afield as Natal, Mauritius, Fiji and Guyana. It also, however unwittingly, set in motion the dispersal of South Asian peoples and cultures into many other corners of the globe. Beginning with the North India famines of the 1840s, which created the impetus for early migration to Mauritius, there remained for most of the rest of the century a clear correlation between bad harvests and peaks of labour

5. Herbert H. Smith, *Brazil, the Amazons and the Coast*, pp. 415-16.

migration. Thus the exodus from southern India to the coffee and tea estates of nearby Sri Lanka (Ceylon) reached its peak in the middle and late 1870s, at a time when a high level of labour demand from the planters was matched by intense drought and famine across the Palk Strait in Madras. In 1876–77 alone, nearly 200,000 labourers left through the province's southern ports, the great majority of them for Sri Lanka.

But it is Ireland which offers the most dramatic illustration of the enormous scale and far-reaching consequences attending famine migration. There had been some migration from Ireland, mostly on a seasonal basis, before the potato famine struck. By the early 1840s upwards of 120,000 Irishmen a year left to spend the summer months as agricultural workers on the other side of the Irish Sea. Only thus could they eke out a living on their tiny farms at home. But the nature and scale of migration changed momentously once the famine began to bite. Without industrial towns or (initially at least) adequate relief measures to stem the migrant tide, with Irish agriculture already deep in crisis, and with the way open by sea for a permanent escape from Ireland, well over a million people left during the course of the potato famine. A quarter of a million departed for North America in 1851 alone, and Irish emigrants continued to pour across the Irish Sea and the Atlantic for decades afterwards. Between 1852 and 1911 nearly five million people left Ireland, three-quarters of them bound for the United States. Any lingering resistance to migration and to proletarianization in the cities of Britain and America was broken by the famine. Entire families, and not just their male members, left for a new life away from the poverty of Ireland.

It was a profound and lasting transformation, and not only for those who left Ireland. Through the departure of so many impoverished tenant farmers, and by the evictions and expulsions that completed the work of the famine, arable land was freed for conversion into pasture, opened up for the capitalist agriculture that was to supersede the peasant and replace the potato. The tiny plots which had once barely supported a family were consolidated into larger holdings, and as a political force as well as a social category poor peasants and tenants all but disappeared from the Irish scene. Through the famine exodus and the continuing departure of the young for New York and Liverpool, Ireland's population fell precipitously from 8.2 million in 1841 and 5.8 million in 1861 to a low of 4.2 million by the 1930s. Migration as much as mortality underscored the colossal impact of famine. But it also showed, too, what lasting and far-reaching effects famine could have upon the subsequent history of a country and a people. Famine could be a transformatory as well as a traumatic event. For all the misery to which the Irish were subjected by the 'Great Hunger', the famine showed that inertia and despair were not the sole response to even so devastating a calamity.

5
Subsistence and the State

In the course of his pioneering discussion, Cornelius Walford remarked that in Britain famine had given rise to 'several of our more important and distinctive institutions'. Among these he included the English Poor Law, as embodied in the Book of Orders of 1587, and the Corn Laws from their origins in the thirteenth century and restoration in 1663 down to their final repeal during the Irish potato famine. He saw a similar relationship between famine and state power emerging half way across the world in British India, where government relief measures had begun with the famines of the 1780s and 1790s. Had Walford been writing even a few years later, he would surely have mentioned the Indian Famine Code of 1880, one of the most significant administrative measures devised during the entire period of British rule in India.

One could go beyond Walford and these specific examples to argue that the fortunes of the state, whether in Europe or in Africa or Asia, have long been closely bound up with the containment or prevention of famine and, more generally, with provisioning the populace. Protecting its subjects from starvation and extreme want has for centuries been one of the primary functions of government and one of the principal public expectations of the state. So central have been ideas of the ruler as the ultimate earthly provider that notions of kingly or state legitimacy have often hinged upon this responsibility. Of course, it is not a simple matter of reciprocity: subjects do not obey their rulers solely in anticipation of being fed in times of need, and rulers have not infrequently found such expectations onerous and impractical. But famine was invariably a testing time for states as well as for people. Public institutions and authorities were placed under considerable strain, and a regime which callously and conspicuously ignored public needs in times of dearth and hunger might well end up by forfeiting its own position. The equation 'food is power', which operated in the rulers' favour in years of plenty, might readily turn against them in leaner times.

Political famine

Before we consider how famine has fostered the growth of govern-
mental power, it will be as well to consider a more negative side to
state involvement. In addition to preventing famines, states have also
perpetrated them, as much as a matter of policy or punishment as
through ignorance or wilful neglect. This has commonly arisen out of
situations where the state is at war with some, perhaps even a
majority, of its subjects, and is most literally true in a civil war situation. One example of this was in Nigeria, following Biafra's abortive
secession in 1967, where hunger was used to force the break-away Ibos
into submission. Destroying crops and pursuing a 'scorched earth'
policy has long been a way of bringing the rebellious to heel. William
the Conqueror's 'harrying of the North' in 1069 was intended to
stamp out lingering resistance to the incorporation of northern
England into the Anglo-Norman domain. And the history of warfare
in medieval and early modern Europe, whether between states or
within them, is replete with tales of pillaging and the destruction of
standing crops to intimidate opponents and force well-fortified towns
into surrender. Until a relatively late date, for want of regular pay and
a military commissariat, soldiers lived off the land. Military campaigns
thus constituted one of 'common accidents' of the medieval age,
adding yet more insecurities to an already precarious peasant
subsistence. A frequent cause of famine, pillaging armies also spread
epidemic diseases in their wake, as during the Thirty Years' War, 'the
classic case study', according to M. W. Flinn, 'of the military
causation of mortality crises'.

Less common, perhaps, were situations where a government, in
order to survive or in pursuit of ideological objectives, sacrificed the
material interests of its subjects in such a way as to precipitate famine
among them. Fear of an impending Japanese invasion prompted the
colonial authorities in Bengal in 1942–43 to destroy boats and
confiscate grain over a wide area of the delta region, further
undermining an already fragile agrarian economy, intensifying the
effects of a poor harvest, and paralyzing the normal movement of foodstuffs into grain-deficient areas. In its determination to feed Calcutta,
to keep vital industries running and ensure that the second city of the
empire did not fall into Japanese hands, the government hauled in
grain stocks from the countryside, thus fuelling inflation and
spreading alarm in rural areas. The mismanagement of an ailing
economy and the sacrifice of agrarian interests to those of the city and

the military lends support to the case for 1943-44 in Bengal as a truly 'man-made' famine.

Russia, too, provides examples of famines that were as much political as climatic or environmental in character. Adverse weather was certainly a contributory factor in the famine of 1891-92, but Tsarist export policies and the dismal legacy of the emancipation of the serfs thirty years earlier, coupled with inadequate relief measures, did much to intensify its impact. Even more striking was the Russian famine of 1932-34 in which several million peasants (by some accounts 5 or 6 million) died not as a result of any climatic freak or Malthusian 'check' but because of virtual civil war between the peasants and the Soviet state.

Peasant discontent had played a significant part in the downfall of the Tsarist state. The failure of the regime to alleviate mass suffering during the 1891-92 famine weakened the authority of the Tsars and drew attention to the peasants' worsening plight. In the countryside the abortive revolution of 1905 took on the character of a peasant jacquerie. But the Bolshevik revolution of 1917 drew its support from the cities rather than from the villages, and the 'food dictatorship' of May 1918 launched a war against the *kulaks*, or rich peasants, accused of being the class enemies of the revolution and holding back the grain desperately needed in the cities. This 'struggle for bread', backed up by armed squads sent out to the countryside to confiscate food for urban consumption, led to a further deterioration in agricultural production. Lenin was forced to retreat from confrontation with the peasantry and at the end of 1920 the policy of requisitioning was abandoned in order to give fresh encouragement to agriculture.

But the peasants' reprieve was shortlived. Drought and famine followed in 1921 with some 25 million peasants affected. Barely had they recovered from this ordeal when Stalin, ignoring the disasters of 1918-21, embarked on a programme of collectivization which renewed the adversarial relationship between the city and the countryside, between the party and the peasants. He was determined to extract as much as possible from the peasants - partly in order to feed the state bureaucracy and the urban workers, but also to pay for the rapid expansion of Russian industry through the export of grain in exchange for foreign machinery. Communist party officials continued to look upon the peasants as *kulaks*, uncommitted to the goals of the new political order and wedded to the conservatism of the pre-revolutionary past. Under the forced collectivization which began in 1929, the state's procurement policies made unrealistically heavy demands which largely ignored peasant needs. Houses and barns were searched and grain stores seized, including the seed grain and fodder needed for peasant agriculture to survive. By these measures vast quantities of grain were amassed for export: 4.8 million tons in 1930; 5.2 million in 1931. But, without enough food to eat, and determined to frustrate further confiscations by passive resistance – concealing what little they had, neglecting crops and livestock rather than allow them to be appropriated by the state – wide areas of southern Russia from the Ukraine and Caucasus to Kazakstan were devastated by famine. Malcolm Muggeridge, no sympathetic observer of the Soviet scene, likened the 'dictatorship of the proletariat' to a plague of locusts, 'taking away or destroying everything edible and leaving behind a barren wilderness'. Unlike in the famines of 1891–92 and 1921, this time foreign food aid was not allowed into Russia. In the confrontation between the peasants and the state, hunger and death were the price of submission. In the end, the peasants were defeated, yielding to superior force though without accepting that the state had a legitimate and prior claim to their produce.

The state as provider

A state at war with its subjects was surely a rare phenomenon. More commonly rulers recognized an identity of interest between them-selves and the people, seeing in the prosperity and contentment of their subjects the surest foundation of their own wealth and power. This was not a moral issue alone. Before there was industry and a sizeable middle class to be taxed, revenue derived from the land was the principal source of income for the state, as it was for the nobility and the Church. Famine and its attendant effects had severe and long-lasting consequences for the recipients of agricultural taxes and dues. The short-term crises of rebellion and secession apart, it was not in their material interest to rule by famine. Even trade and manufac-turing in a society still essentially pre-industrial in character were likely to suffer the repercussions of famine through the loss of agricultural raw materials and the shrinkage of purchasing power and domestic markets.

Hunger and impoverishment brought about by excessive taxation were likely harbingers of revolt, as many a tax-hungry monarch of the sixteenth and seventeenth centuries, anxious for funds to maintain a costly court and an expanding bureaucracy and army, was forced to acknowledge. One reason, for example, for the weakening of the Mughal empire in India under Aurangzeb in the later part of the seventeenth century was the increasing tax burden which gave peasants and landlords a common reason to grow restive and revolt. When peasants did not revolt they fled. In India before the mid-nineteenth century a great deal of land remained unoccupied, and a ruler who asked too much in revenue and drove his subjects to the brink of starvation was likely to find the peasants migrating to less heavily taxed domains or to uncultivated wastes and wildernesses. Through his greed he was left without subjects to tax or cultivators to till the soil.

In the world of pre-modern agriculture, labour control was the key to resource exploitation. Land without peasants to work it was next to useless. The 'real basis of wealth' in the thinly populated Europe of the seventh and eighth centuries, according to Georges Duby, 'was not ownership of land but power over men'. Partly from the practical necessity of maintaining a stable and productive labour force, though also in order to preserve a wider authority and fulfil a Christian obligation to charity, kings, nobles and landlords helped out their dependants in times of dearth with gifts of food and grain.

Promoting the idea of the state as the protector and provider of the poor also had its political rewards. It served, as in the Carolingian age, to exalt the power of the ruler and stressed his role as intermediary between god and man. It enhanced his authority over his subjects and his prestige among his peers and neighbours. It balanced coercion, always a problematic instrument of state power over the long term and especially in the weakly articulated political systems of the pre-modern era, with a willing (or at least sullen) submission to the hegemony of the monarch and the ruling classes. The state, or its local representative, could be seen to rise above the greedy self-interest of profiteering traders, and to stand for a morality higher than money-making. By remitting taxes in times of dearth (or, like many a medieval authority, by ordering traders to sell at fixed prices or prohibiting the brewing of beer when grain was in short supply), rulers both laid claim to a paternalistic authority of their own and acknowledged a broad responsibility for the subsistence needs of their people.

If we look for evidence of the state as a provider of famine relief and an agency of famine control, China offers striking illustration. 'Until recent times', according to Paul Bohr, 'few governments have professed as much concern for the welfare of their people as the government of China'. Although the ideology of the Confucian state emphasized the strict subordination of the peasantry to the scholar-gentry elite and contrasted peasant barbarity and ignorance with mandarin learning and refinement, peasants were none the less valued

as the indispensable basis of China's economy and society. In return
for their compliance (and as a means of ensuring its own survival) the
state showed great concern for the peasants' material wellbeing. The
Manchu emperors, it was said, were fully 'aware that the best way to
ensure adequate revenue was to conserve the people's ability to pay
taxes'. This appreciation of the value of the peasants to the state, as
self-interested as it was clear-sighted, accounts in part for the
remarkable longevity of China's imperial state. But by relying so
heavily upon the peasants as the primary source of revenue and as the
foundation for a stable political order, each dynasty also bound its
fortunes inextricably to those of the peasants. So much so that a
peasantry goaded to rebellion by discontent and hunger might hold a
dagger to the throat of its imperial master.

Confucianism enjoined officials to be the 'father and mother of the
people', just as the emperor himself, as the 'Son of Heaven', offered
up prayers for an abundant harvest or for the cessation of drought and
floods. State paternalism was a recognition, too, of the hazardous
nature of the Chinese environment and hence of the need for an
administration able to protect the peasants from the worst effects of
natural disasters and to direct measures for the prevention and relief of
famine. Officials supervized the maintenance of river dykes and the
dredging of rivers to prevent flooding. Agricultural colonization and
improvement were encouraged, and granaries established to provide
relief in times of hunger.

But Confucian paternalism was also a form of insurance against the
insecurities inherent in a peasant-based polity. China's peasantry bore
a Janus face. For most of the time quiescent, compliant, the epitome of
hardwork, thrift and endurance, the peasants were also as capable as
the Yellow River of bursting through their constricting banks and
unleashing a pent-up, destructive fury. Just as China's gentry elite
gained cohesion through its examination system, official honours,
bureaucratic powers and paternalistic ideology, so the peasants gathered strength from the secret societies, the bandit armies, and the
millenarian sects which flourished among them. From time to time
these diverse forces merged together in massive peasant movements
that surged across China and which, once in every few hundred years,
helped to sweep away an imperial dynasty in their flood. The gentry
and the emperors accordingly watched with well-founded anxiety for
signs that presaged revolt. From the earliest times natural disasters
were interpreted in China by rulers and peasants alike as manifes-
tations of cosmic disorder. They saw in them signs that a dynasty had
lost the 'mandate of heaven' and that its demise was imminent. It was

thus from political self-interest, not idle curiosity, that China's rulers duly noted each flood and famine in the local annals and official histories and recorded the measures taken in anticipation or alleviation. A calamity was a heaven-sent omen, but it was also an earthly event encroaching upon the knife-edge existence of many millions of peasants, and as such capable of impelling them to violence, banditry and revolt. A competent and energetic dynasty would move rapidly in response to the crisis and devise or implement effective relief measures. Better still, it would already have ensured that the river dykes were in good order and the granaries full. It would act swiftly to suppress the first rumblings of revolt and to minimize the damage to state revenues and imperial authority. But a weak dynasty, misled by sycophants, blinkered by complacency, or already creaking from its own ineptitude and corruption, would be unable either to anticipate disaster or to respond promptly when it announced its arrival. Imperial weakness and lethargy would then encourage further revolts, carrying a section of disgruntled gentry with them or opening the door to external invasion. China had seen this sequence of events, this massive testing of imperial might and resolution, many times in its history. As early as the T'ang dynasty in the ninth century AD severe and widespread famine bred revolt and pitched a once-flourishing dynasty to its fall. The Ming suffered a similar fate in the mid-seventeenth century: on this occasion the invasion of the Manchus from the northeast completed the work peasant rebellion had already begun within China itself.

Building on the statutes (and the experiences) of previous dynasties, the Manchus, once firmly established in power, authorized a series of famine-control measures. These included land reclamation and water conservancy, the 'eradication of pests' including locusts and 'flood dragons', the provision of emergency relief in the form of food and money for those stricken by inundation and famine, the sale of grain at reduced rates or the grant of food loans to the destitute, exemption and deferment of taxes, encouragement to merchants to import grain into deficit areas, public relief works, and schemes for the rehabilitation of refugees. Under a dynasty at the height of its powers some or all of these measures might be put into operation. In a famine in 1493 Ming officials distributed half-a-million silver taels and 2 million piculs of grain in Shantung, thus helping to save the lives of over two million hungry people.

A critical element in the precautionary schemes taken up by the Manchus was the maintenance of public granaries. In addition to those that held grain exclusively to feed Peking, granaries were set up in all of China's cities and districts. Grain for these came from special imperial quotas supplemented by local levies and voluntary contributions. Fresh grain was to be purchased annually to replenish stores so that in times of shortage peasants and town-dwellers could be provided with loans or gifts of grain. Once again elite self-interest was not absent as a motive. 'To protect the poor is tantamount to protecting the rich', was a common expression among the gentry. Experience had shown that a full reserve of grain was 'one of the best means of maintaining imperial peace in times of stress'. The system seems to have worked tolerably well during the heyday of Manchu power: indeed, the eighteenth century has been called the 'golden age' of famine relief in China. Along with other preventive and remedial measures, the granary system enabled China to avoid demographic catastrophe despite its steadily rising population. But by the early decades of the nineteenth century the Manchu administration was becoming demonstrably weaker at the very time when demographic pressure and land hunger were making unprecedented demands on the economy and the state. Through neglect and peculation by corrupt members of the gentry, granaries were found when needed to be empty or half-filled with old, musty and inedible grain. The Manchu court, casting about for scapegoats, blamed the breakdown of the granary system for the early successes of the Taipings. But the eventual defeat of the rebellion brought no significant improvement in famine prevention and relief measures.

The Chinese authorities tried to meet the massive famine of the late 1870s with the distribution of money and grain and with tax exemptions, but the amounts given – dismissed by western observers as a 'mere pittance' – failed to prevent many millions of deaths from starvation. In itself the famine was but one of the many economic, social and political disasters which sapped the administration's energy and undermined its prestige. The growth of western relief, which began in earnest with the 1876–79 famine and continued intermittently until the 1930s, further called in question the traditional authority and administrative capacity of the gentry and the imperial system. Famine after famine pronounced Confucian paternalism bankrupt since it had defaulted on even its most basic obligation – to meet the subsistence needs of China's peasant poor. This redundancy, not unlike that of the Russian Tsars at about the same time, fuelled opposition to the Manchus and helped bring about their fall in the revolution of 1911.

However, their Nationalist successors proved little more effective. The old granary system was swept away, but in a China divided by warlords and plagued by militarism nothing adequate took its place. The idealism of Sun Yat-sen and the Kuomintang, who had declared the 'people's livelihood' to be one of their three basic principles, failed to bring China's peasants the promised relief and reform. Instead it was the Communist Party, in moving under Mao Tse-tung from the cities to the countryside, which took up the cause of peasant hunger. During the Honan famine of 1942–43, which had been greatly exacerbated by the indifference of warlords and the officials' embezzlement, the Communists in areas under their control combined relief with practical measures to reform landholding and increase agricultural production. In their concern for peasant welfare, the Communists were heirs to the Confucian paternalist tradition; but they combined this with the structural reform of agrarian society which alone could give back to China the capacity to feed itself. Famine-control was likewise one of the first priorities of the new Communist state after the revolution of 1949 and seemingly one of its great successes – until the famine of 1958–61 cruelly exposed the technological and political limitations of China's agrarian revolution.

Poor laws and corn laws

China was in some ways exceptional. Famine was more frequent and more devastating there than in the experience of most of Europe after the seventeenth century. The well-rehearsed progression from hunger to rebellion and dynastic overthrow (which itself had few direct European parallels) had endowed China's rulers with a singular sensitivity to the political nuances of natural disasters. But the exceptionality of China was not so great as might at first sight appear. It was a European monarch, Louis XIV of France, who observed in his memoirs that 'the need for food is the first thing a prince should consider', a dictum that found some confirmation, three-quarters of a century after the Sun King's death, in the revolution of 1789. It can, indeed, be argued that in the European context the need to mitigate famine and provision the people was one of the most important factors behind the rise of the modern state, just as the neglect of this responsibility exposed regimes to some of their most serious challenges.

In medieval times European states did what little they could in an age of poor overland transport and undeveloped markets to avert the threat of famine. The provisioning of cities, with their tendency to gobble up food supplies for many miles around, was always a problem and assumed great political and economic urgency in times of dearth. It has been argued that the difficulty of obtaining sufficient food for expanding urban populations was an important constraint on urban growth or, as in the case of London, was only made possible by the development of commercial farming over a wide area of the surrounding countryside. Cities tried to meet the threat of famine by importing grain by sea. Bruges in the Low Countries, for example, negotiated substantial wheat imports from the Mediterranean in 1317, and, during that same time of hunger, England's Edward II promised safe conduct to foreign merchants to import grain from famine-free Italy and southern France. Municipal authorities and city states attempted to prohibit the export or hoarding of grain and obliged butchers and bakers to sell at fixed prices and in approved weights and measures. Out of these *ad hoc* measures grew many more permanent statutes and regulations about food pricing and marketing and a more enduring municipal or state commitment to price controls and provisioning. In the short-term, however, cities were sometimes driven to such desperate expedients as seizing the cargoes of any passing grain-ship they could lay their hands on. Fernand Braudel[1] noted that in the Mediterranean world of the late sixteenth century:

> When famine threatened, the measures taken were everywhere identical. To the sound of trumpets it was forbidden to take grain out of the town, the guard was doubled, searches were conducted and available supplies were inventoried. If the danger increased sterner measures were taken: The number of mouths to feed was reduced, the city gates were closed, or else foreigners were expelled, the normal course in Venice, unless they had brought enough grain into the city to feed their staff or household . . . After that, rationing was generally introduced . . .

As Europe crossed from medieval into modern times, the problems of provisioning increased. Cities grew in size, doubling in their total population between 1500 and 1700, then again between 1700 and 1850, and once more (through the impetus of accelerating industrialization) between 1850 and 1914. As Europe's emerging nation states consolidated their territories and expanded their administrative and military power, they spawned vast bureaucracies as well as armies which (from about the time of Louis XIV) were no longer expected simply to live off the land. All these mouths had somehow to be fed,

1. *The Mediterranean and the Mediterranean World in the Age of Philip II*, vol. 1, p. 330.

and for political reasons their provisioning was a high priority of state. Laws and regulations of various kinds were devised to ease the flow of food from the countryside to the cities.

The other great pressure for state intervention – in Europe as in China – was the threat of disorder. There was alarm at the growth of crime and vagrancy in England during the famine of 1315–22, but the perceived threat to property and order was even greater in the late sixteenth century when the 'Great Hunger' of 1594–96 swelled the ranks of an already sizeable population of vagrants and paupers and sparked incipient revolt in several parts of the country. From scarcity of corn, it was said, 'the poor died from starvation or rose in insurrection'. When local measures for the control of vagrancy proved wholly inadequate to meet this crisis, the Tudor state, in one of the many extensions of its power, was forced to intervene directly. The Book of Orders of 1587, reissued in 1594, not only helped Elizabeth's government to counter the problem of vagrancy and destitution. It also became the basis for the English Poor Law of subsequent centuries. Before this legislative milestone, E. M. Leonard claimed in 1900 in her *Early History of English Poor Relief*, England had been 'repeatedly disturbed by rebellions and constantly plagued by vagrants'. Thereafter, following the institution of the Poor Law, England was blessed with 'orderly government', and, she added with a meaningful glance across the Channel, 'it may be that our legal system of poor relief has ever since contributed to the absence of violent catastrophe in our national history'. An extravagant claim, no doubt; certainly an unverifiable one. But Leonard's remarks at least point to famine's importance in forcing state intervention and prompting institutional responses that, in their turn, might be of immense social and political significance. It could be added that England's corn laws, too, although largely designed to encourage exports in good years, also served as recognition of the state's ultimate responsibility for ensuring the adequate supply, if necessary through importation, of corn in years of deficient domestic harvests.

In France, as in other parts of the Europe of the *ancien régime*, food was of immense political significance. Steven L. Kaplan notes the persistence of the idea, which some eighteenth-century commentators traced back to Charlemagne, 'that the king had a duty to safeguard the existence and therefore the subsistence of his subjects'. Though never a formal attribute of kingship in France, the notion of the monarch as the 'supreme victualler' was a powerfully enduring one, if only because it lay so close to the collective hopes and subsistence fears of the mass of the country's poor. The women who marched on Versailles in October 1789 still continued to see the king as the 'victualler of last resort'.

As with other governments of the *ancien régime*, too, the problems of grain distribution and marketing were a perennial source of anxiety to the French administration. In particular, the provisioning of Paris, the most politically sensitive city in France as well as much the largest, was one of the major preoccupations of both the monarchy and its revolutionary successors of 1789. Attempting to feed Paris, Richard Cobb remarks in *The People's Armies*, was above all 'a question of public order and one that tested the effectiveness of any regime', especially as, added to the 'material difficulties hindering the circulation and distribution of grain and other foodstuffs at any time', was the 'more serious human one inspired by fear and rumour'. Consignments of grain moving by road or canal were very likely in times of unrest and dearth to be plundered by the local poor long before they could reach their destination in Paris.

It was indicative of the political importance of provisioning urban centres and capital cities like Paris that one of the first and foremost duties of state policing (in its broad eighteenth-century sense of public regulation) was to control the markets and to supervize the supply and pricing of food. This also entailed, as Cobb's comment suggests, keeping in close touch with the mood of the people, reporting on the rumours of profiteering and speculation that circulated in market-places and inns, listening to the talk of dearth and hunger that might, unchecked, flare up into riot, revolution or counter-revolution. When violence did occur from such causes it was the task of Europe's emerging police forces and gendarmeries (as well as troops and levies of all descriptions) to quell them. In thus providing an incentive for the creation of civilian or paramilitary constabularies, famine and hunger were again responsible for institutional innovations of lasting significance. But hunger, it must be added, also had its uses for those in power. Without the pressure of want in the less prosperous regions of France (as in comparable parts of Scotland and Ireland), without the appeal of a military meal-ticket for the famished and the needy, the armies of eighteenth and early nineteenth century Europe would have been hard-pressed to find the peasant recruits on which their infantry regiments so heavily depended.

When governments failed persistently to attend to the subsistence needs of the poor there was every danger that the situation would grow beyond the capacity of the police and magistracy to control. The

French Revolution of 1789 represents something of a paradox in these terms. The time has hopefully passed when historians seek to explain periods of revolution and reaction simply in terms of the rise and fall of food prices. Clearly the French Revolution was something more than a spontaneous response or a 'knee-jerk' reaction to the soaring price of bread. The social and political frustrations of the middle classes, the deepening constitutional crisis, the dwindling prestige of the king and his ministers, the failure of moderate reform and the growth of ideas critical of absolutism – all these combined to create a heady cocktail of political discontent. But as one of the many underlying causes, as one of the key factors responsible for integrating popular revolt into a wider political movement, famine (or, more exactly, fear of famine) was far from insignificant.

Despite periodic high prices and shortages, there had been no real famine in France since 1709, or possibly 1740, partly because of improvements in transportation and government efforts to establish greater freedom in the marketing of foodstuffs. But if not famine there was still extreme poverty and widespread hunger, especially in the lean years of 1740, 1749, 1768, 1775, and 1785. The numbers of the poor in the towns and in the countryside appear to have grown enormously, creating a large class of near-destitutes for whom subsistence was a daily struggle to earn, steal or beg enough to eat. Famine in its old recurrent and acute form may have disappeared, but its spectre still stalked the land. In the countryside many poor peasants held plots of land too small to feed their families even when harvests were good. In an age when bread was still truly synonymous with food, a great number of labourers and sharecroppers were vitally dependent on the market for their daily sustenance. In the towns craftsmen and labourers shared the nervous anxiety of rural consumers over the availability and price of bread which could cost them half or more of their meagre income. For these small producers and market-dependent consumers, the years 1787–89 spelt catastrophe. Bad harvests brought the worst shortages for decades and revived the prospect of mass starvation. The price of wheat doubled and by mid-1789 had reached record levels over almost the whole of France. Peasants, urban craftsmen and workers were thus thrown together in common hostility to the merchants and the speculators who controlled the price of bread and to the landlords and nobles who were thought to be hoarding grain. This alarm over basic subsistence needs, once added to the developing political ferment, helped make the revolution of 1789.

The trials of laissez-faire

As domestic and international transport links improved and as agriculture became more productive and increasingly market-oriented, the governments of western Europe sought to free themselves of the age-old obligation to feed the people and regulate the markets. In France in 1763–64 the government of Louis XVI broke with tradition and with unwritten covenant to disclaim any further responsibility for the grain trade. In this way, Kaplan remarks, 'The consumers lost their privileged identity as *the* people as grain lost its privileged status in commerce and public life.' In France, however, this attempt to make subsistence a matter of individual rather than state concern was short-lived. Overtaken by the subsistence crisis of the late 1760s the government was forced to retreat from its 'liberalizing' moves. In Britain, however, ideas of Free Trade gained increasing momentum in the late eighteenth century and the early years of the nineteenth, buoyed up by the growing productivity of agriculture and by the strength of expanding industry and international commerce. In 1814–15 the Corn Laws, the last bastion of the old protectionist and paternalist economy, were amended, and in 1846, under Sir Robert Peel, finally swept away. By that date, 'practically all public men [in Britain] were imbued with the belief that market forces should not be tampered with, that self-reliance must not be weakened or local effort superseded by the activities of the Government'.

The triumph of *laissez-faire* signalled a profound revolution in state responsibilities. For centuries the state or the monarch had been viewed as the ultimate provider of the people in times of direst need, and though this expectation had often passed unfulfilled, it had never been emphatically denied as it was by the early nineteenth century. This reversal was all the more remarkable in that ideas of *laissez-faire* as they affected the supply and marketing of grain gained ascendancy at a time when the state in Britain in particular was taking responsibility for many other aspects of public welfare from sanitation to factory hours and working conditions and, latterly, even education and provision for the aged and sick. Seen in this light, the denial of government responsibility for food provisioning stands out as an extraordinary anomaly.

Something of the political as well as economic magnitude of this revolution in state policy was made apparent in the writings of that arch-apostle of Free Trade, Adam Smith. In a 'Digression on the Corn

Trade' in the course of his *Wealth of Nations* of 1776, Smith deplored the way in which governments in the past had been (as he saw it) held to ransom by the unreasoning and unwarranted clamour of the mob. It was as if, he suggested, foolish suspicions of witchcraft had been allowed to persist into the modern age, with the grain traders cast as the target of witch-hunts and with the government obliged to yield to the people's 'prejudices' simply for the sake of public tranquillity. In complete contrast to the popular view of grain traders and merchants as predators profiting from the needs of the poor, Smith argued that their interests were broadly commensurate with those of the community they served. In years of good harvests they gleaned little profit from the abundance of corn, and only in times of poor harvest were they able to reap a just reward for their enterprise. The intervention of the state, or the even more harmful intercession of the mob, which seized food or demanded bread at absurdly low prices, robbed merchants of their legitimate income and discouraged the influx of food supplies from elsewhere. Without prices being allowed to rise to higher levels there would be no incentive for traders to import grain and dearth would then indeed become a famine. A rise in prices was, to Smith, a desirable and necessary market mechanism, too, in that it encouraged customers to be frugal in their food consumption rather than rapidly eating up the little that was available and thus hastening the advent of extreme want. Smith did not deny that famines could occur, but he argued that in recent centuries (wars apart) Europe had experienced dearth only as a result of the 'fault of the seasons', not through any combination of corn dealers. A drought, such as that which had recently occurred in Bengal, Smith suggested with a dig at the monopolistic East India Company, had only turned into a famine because of the 'improper regulations' and 'injudicious restraints' imposed upon the movement and pricing of grain by local officials. The 'unlimited, unrestrained freedom of the corn trade' was thus confidently declared to be not only 'the best palliative of the inconveniences of a dearth', but also the 'only effectual preventative of a famine' when such a situation arose.

Smith's economic reasoning was not without its political ironies. On the one hand governments were sternly rebuked for meddling in the grain trade and for not allowing market forces to operate free from artificial constraint. But, stripped of its ancient role as 'victualler of last resort', the state was summoned back as policeman instead, for how else could the freedom of trade be guaranteed but by the presence of policemen and soldiers to prevent or discourage looting and seizures of grain? 'No trade', remarked Smith in passing of the grain trade, 'deserves more the full protection of the law, and no trade requires it so much; because no trade is so much exposed to popular odium'. In shedding the responsibility of the seigneur and the monarch to feed his people, the state was, however, reinventing paternalism in a new and sterner form. The state – or, in a new age of bureaucratic government, the intellectuals, the economists and the officials who spoke on its behalf – claimed to possess a better understanding of the real interests of the people than the people themselves. Their fears of speculation, hoarding and dearth were unfounded, irrational, and primitive, tainted with the superstitions of a bygone age. It was their reckless folly, not the operation of market forces, that was held most likely to transform inconvenient shortages into severe famine. The profligacy and irrationality of the poor could only be checked through the operation of laws, whether by allowing the laws of economics to function unimpeded or through the protection provided by the laws of the country on behalf of the traders and against the depredations of the people.

Even in England the transition from 'moral economy' to 'political economy' did not pass uncontested. There were the widespread food riots of the 1750s and 1760s to attest to that, and as late as the 1830s the passionate slogan 'Bread or Blood' echoed around the English countryside. Not until the mid-nineteenth century, with the further progress of the Industrial Revolution and increasing food imports from overseas, did the spectre of famine finally recede as if for ever. But at least in England Free Trade grew, as it were, organically out of the country's changing economy. It was otherwise elsewhere where *laissez-faire* smacked of a foreign imposition inappropriate to the needs and the times.

In Ireland, in the late 1840s, the chief famine administrator, C. E. Trevelyan, made no secret of the fact that he saw the famine as a blessing in disguise. For him it was 'the direct stroke of an all-wise Providence', a heaven-sent solution to the otherwise intractable problem of Ireland's poverty and backwardness. It was a 'great opportunity' to rid Ireland of an idle and unproductive peasantry and to replace it with a class of educated landed proprietors of the kind he saw as having brought prosperity to agriculture on the other side of the Irish Sea. Such a view was itself unconducive to substantial government intervention to relieve peasant suffering, but Trevelyan was also staunchly committed to ideas of strict economy in government expenditure and a firm believer in the new orthodoxy of 'sound political economy'. With *laissez-faire* fast gaining ground at Westminster, too, and Peel, the Prime Minister, increasingly persuaded of its virtues, grain continued to be shipped out of Ireland at the same time that many tens of thousands of people were starving there for want of food. Peel's administration was not altogether inert in the face of this unfolding tragedy. Steps were taken to provide work so that labourers could buy their own food, and in November 1845 Peel authorized the purchase of £100,000 worth of maize from the United States in order to prevent private traders from exploiting an absolute monopoly but without creating direct (and thus unacceptable) government competition.

The Whig ministry of Lord John Russell, installed after Peel's departure from office in the summer of 1846 and following the final overthrow of the Corn Laws, was even more fervent in its attachment to Free Trade. Despite the worsening crisis in Ireland, the new Prime Minister (who declined even to speak of famine, preferring to call it a 'scarcity') believed that the state's role should be strictly confined to providing employment on public (and, where possible, non-productive) works and that the costs of relief should fall on Irish, not English, shoulders. Even for the most needy free relief was seen to be highly undesirable, likely to encourage indolence and build up a class of state-dependent paupers for the future, as well as interfering with existing wage levels and terms of employment. The Whigs were only forced into great intervention by the increasingly massive scale of destitution evident by early 1847. The number of people in receipt of relief rose from a quarter of a million to almost three-quarters between October 1846 and the spring of the following year. Emergency outdoor relief was belatedly instituted, though even then a significant part of the relief, especially through soup kitchens, was left to voluntary organizations like the Quakers. By the end of 1848, with the worst of the famine over, the state, for all its parsimony, had spent nearly £8 million on Irish relief. Had it acted sooner and more generously many lives and much suffering might have been spared. Ireland paid a heavy price for England's commitment to *laissez-faire*.

In India, too, the East India Company administration swung around quickly to the new economic orthodoxy. This was partly through the influence exercised upon its servants by T. R. Malthus, elevated from country parson to become Professor of Political Economy at the Company's college at Haileybury in 1805. But ideas of non-intervention by the state also had a practical appeal in India, as in Ireland, to a colonial administration anxious to minimize all possible expenditure and only grudgingly growing aware of the immensity of the task it had undertaken. S. Ambirajan has argued that in India Malthusian theories of population and 'natural checks' combined with the doctrines of Adam Smith to encourage an exceptionally negative attitude towards famine and its alleviation. The argument in effect was, 'What is the use of saving lives when once again the people so saved would suffer later in the same way?'

During the famines and shortages of the early and mid-nineteenth century, the provincial governments adhered firmly to the principles of Free Trade, reproving officials who tried to fix market prices or who sided with hungry and frightened consumers against the grain traders. A statement first circulated by the Board of Revenue in Madras in 1811 and reissued several times thereafter quoted almost verbatim from *The Wealth of Nations* to explain the folly of state intervention. There was to be no interference with trade. High prices were desirable in that they discouraged people from consuming grain 'in a greater quantity than is absolutely necessary' and provided the essential stimulus for private trade. Although this policy might provoke 'the outrages of the people', such demonstrations of 'impatience' at their 'trifling inconvenience' were to be firmly suppressed in order to give merchants the confidence and freedom to trade. A similar statement prepared by John Strachey as Collector of Moradabad in the North-Western Provinces in 1861, deprecating any attempt by officials to import or reduce the prices of grain during scarcities, was quoted with approval during the 1866 famine in Orissa and commended in the Government of India's own statement on famine policy two years later. The Viceroy of the day 'most earnestly impress[ed] upon all persons in authority the necessity for not permitting the smallest interference with the ordinary operations of trade during the continuance of scarcity.'

But India was not Ireland. Ideas and institutions which, for all their unsuitability, were imposed upon Ireland under the eye of Westminster, were received more cautiously half a world away. It became evident, particularly during the heavy mortality of the 1860s and 1870s that a policy of *laissez-faire* alone could not meet the extreme and (unlike in Ireland) recurrent crises of Indian famine. Arthur Cotton, who in the wake of the devastating Guntur famine of 1833, had brought irrigation to the once-arid lands of the Godavari delta, urged the state to undertake similar schemes as a protection against crop failures in other parts of the country. Sir William Hunter, reflecting on the Orissa famine of 1866, drew up figures to show how much that catastrophe had cost the state in relief and lost revenues compared to what could have been saved by investing in irrigation and other preventive works. Others argued for state-sponsored railways to stimulate agricultural production and as a means of moving food rapidly into drought-stricken areas.

Without formally violating the precepts of Free Trade the government began to take on greater responsibility for famine relief and control, if only because of the serious threat posed to its revenue from the land. While the general principle of non-intervention in the grain trade remained inviolate until the Second World War, other areas of state involvement were considered to be legitimate for the creation of an economic infrastructure in a country where enterprise and capital were otherwise apparently lacking. Irrigation received some state support though, to Cotton's dismay, considerably less than the railway system developed in India in the post-Mutiny decades. The construction of the railways, especially the feeder-lines that helped to transport grain into the remoter and more arid areas, in the end played a critical part in the containment of famine in the sub-continent (though their role short-term was more ambiguous for they also aided the export of grain from needy districts to those where prices reigned still higher).

There was other evidence, too, of a growing, if still very qualified, sense of state responsibility for famine prevention and relief. In his minute on famine policy of August 1877 the Viceroy, Lord Lytton, stated that the government would abstain from involving itself in the grain trade 'so long as that trade was active'. However, it would endeavour to 'avert death from starvation' through public works and all other means 'practically open to the resources of the State and the exertions of its officers', though, he added, in a significant rider, that it would attempt to 'discharge this duty at the lowest cost compatible with the preservation of human life from wholesale destruction'. The Famine Code drafted in 1880 gave guidance as to how administrators might anticipate famine by responding to the first signs of impending distress (in particular when grain prices rose to 'famine levels') and how they should act to alleviate suffering, if necessary by providing gratuitous relief to needy villagers in their homes as well as on public relief works. Tax remissions and loans were authorized to enable cultivators to recover from the worst effects of drought and restart agricultural operations as quickly as possible. In practice, not all these well-intended guide-lines were acted upon or brought adequate results. Revenue concessions and loans, for example, were often too niggardly to compensate for heavy famine losses. None the less, for all its shortcomings and the heavy famine mortality that recurred in the late 1890s and early 1900s, British famine policy by the late nineteenth century was edging significantly further and further away from the initial standpoint of *laissez-faire*. The Famine Code formed part of a move, however hesitant, towards greater state responsibility for the Indian economy and for the welfare of the mass of the Indian people.

Famine and the critique of state power

The more that famine came to be viewed as something that was not god-given or solely the consequence of natural causes but as man-made or amenable to human amelioration and intervention, the more famine began to form part of a developing critique of state power. This was especially so in colonial territories like Ireland and India, where British policies seemed most at variance with local needs and where famine gained a prominent place in the emerging rhetoric of nationalism. But famine had a comparable role elsewhere – for example, in the mounting domestic and international criticisms of the Tsarist regime in Russia in the 1890s and early 1900s. After all, what greater indictment could there be of a government than to claim that it had, whether from indifference to suffering or from blind adherence to abstract principles, neglected the subsistence needs of the people and thus been responsible for the death of millions of its subjects?

In some respects the famine in Ireland left the British administration more powerfully entrenched than ever. With the death or departure of the poor tenant farmers, the earlier movements of peasant protest and agrarian agitation swiftly collapsed. Even Daniel O'Connell's movement for the repeal of the Act of Union faded away, 'its last echoes drowned in the cries of a starving peasantry'. But if the 'Great Hunger' saw the demise of one agitation, it in turn gave birth to another. Most historians would now absolve the government in Westminster of direct responsibility for the Irish tragedy (though many continue to blame the British for doing too little too late to help the starving). But for decades afterwards the famine served as a conclusive demonstration of Britain's brutal indifference to Irish suffering and an incontestable argument that an independent Ireland would be a happier and more prosperous land. England's responsibility for the death and misery of millions became an essential part of the mythology of Irish nationalism, comparable, perhaps, in emotive terms to the Jewish Holocaust almost a century later. In the Irish perception the English emerged from the episode, Herman Ausubel has remarked, as 'monsters who preached and acted on the inhuman doctrine that the best thing for Ireland was to permit the Famine to wipe out a large section of the population'. Certainly 'the calamitous years burnt themselves deep into the imagination of the [Irish] people and', F. S. L. Lyons adds, 'have haunted their descendents ever since.'

In 1848, that year of revolutions, the Young Ireland leader Charles Gavan Duffy declared that the famine was a 'fearful murder committed on the mass of the people', while in similar vein Arthur Griffith later alleged that the British government had used 'the pretext of the failure of the potato crop to reduce the Celtic population by famine and exile'. The more perceptive of British observers at the time could see that the famine was creating a legacy of hatred between Britain and Ireland. The Radical John Bright remarked in the House of Commons in August 1848 that 'in whatever quarter of the world an Irishman sets his foot, there stands a bitter, an implacable enemy of England'. The migration of tens of thousands of Irish men and women to the United States and the resentment against Britain that lived on amongst them there bore out the truth of this claim. Twenty years after the 'Great Hunger' the Fenian rising of 1867 showed how fiercely the memory of the famine still burned among Irish exiles in America. The 'Great Hunger' both nourished and symbolized Irish hatred of British rule.

In India, too, British responsibility for famine became no less important an article of nationalist faith. The severe and recurrent famines of the late nineteenth century coincided with, and in part helped to stimulate, the growth of a nationalist critique of colonial rule. Famine figured prominently in the formulation (and contributed greatly to the emotional force) of the nationalists' 'Drain Theory', which saw in famine tangible evidence that the wealth of a once prosperous India had been stripped from the country under British rule – by conquest and plunder, by the destruction of India's manufactures and trades, by excessive land revenue demands and the heavy administrative costs India was forced to bear. One of the principal exponents of this theory, Dadabhai Naoroji, made frequent reference to famines in his book *Poverty and Un-British Rule in India*, published in 1901 at a time when much of India was reeling under the effects of widespread hunger, and on his lecture tours of England, using them to counter the Malthusian argument of the administrators that over-population, not British mismanagement, was the root cause of India's misery. The Drain Theory found another powerful advocate in R. C. Dutt, who in his *Economic History of India*, argued that 'the evil of a perpetual economic drain from India' had made the country 'a land of poverty and famines'. Famines in India, he conceded, were 'directly due to a deficiency in the annual rainfall', but their intensity and the loss of life they caused were 'largely due to the chronic poverty of the people'. If the people were in a generally prosperous condition they could have made up for local crop failures by purchasing grain from neighbouring provinces, Dutt argued, and there would have been no loss of life. But, he said, the excessive burden of land revenue payments had left the people 'absolutely resourceless'. Hence, 'they cannot buy from surrounding tracts, and . . . perish in hundreds of thousands, or in millions, whenever there is a local failure of crops.'

In similar vein but at a slightly earlier date, the Indian National Congress at its annual session in 1896 passed two resolutions linking Indian poverty with excessive taxation and administrative extravagance. One of the resolutions, echoing the government's own declared objectives, stated that the state had a 'solemn duty to save human life and mitigate human suffering'. But it also urged on the government a policy of retrenchment to 'husband the resources of the state', support for indigenous crafts, 'which [had] practically been extinguished', and help towards the 'introduction of modern arts and industries'. This was considerably further than the government of the day, for all its famine codes and relief measures, was yet prepared to go.

The experience of famine and the broad agreement among nationalists as to British culpability, had an enduring effect on the outlook and aspirations of India's nationalist movement and its leaders. The mass poverty and suffering made evident through famine forced middle-class nationalists to pay greater attention to the plight of the peasantry. By the immensity of their suffering, India's famine-struck peasants wrote themselves into the nationalists' as well as the colonialists' agenda. Gandhi, with his loin-cloth and spinning-wheel and with his determination to revive the cottage industries of village India, showed his way of identifying with the plight of the peasantry and offered one possible line of escape from the rural poverty which, he believed, British rule and its attendant evils had helped to bring about. But Gandhi's was not the only nationalist riposte. Jawaharlal Nehru, who from his imprisonment in Ahmadnagar Fort in 1944 commented bitterly on the Bengal famine as the final tragic act in Britain's long history of 'indifference, incompetence, and complacency' towards the people of India, saw the need for a very different solution. Especially once he had become the first Prime Minister of post-Independence India, Nehru argued that the country's future lay in following the West's own escape route from dearth and hunger through industrialization, building up India's manufacturing base and freeing it from external economic as well as political dependency. The state, for Gandhi an anathema, was for Nehru the agency (once properly harnessed and made subservient to the needs of the people) through which real economic and social progress could be achieved. Famine was thus not only part of the critique of colonial rule, a stick with which to beat the British for their exploitation and cruelty. It also had the effect of forcing nationalists like Gandhi and Nehru to think about an alternative political order and about economic strategies that could provide an enduring freedom from want.

6
Other People's Hunger

In the first centuries of western expansionism the world beyond Europe's shores represented a world of riches. Europe was motivated by many things – curiosity and Christian zeal among them. But it was primarily in search of wealth (and the fame and position it brought) that Europeans launched themselves upon strange oceans, uncertain of their safe return. They sought to share in the riches, real or imagined, of the rest of the globe. In the Americas Spanish conquistadores sought the legendary El Dorado. In Africa the Portuguese dreamed of the Christian kingdom of Prester John, wealthy and powerful enough to aid them in their interminable struggle against the Moors of Islam. But it was above all the Orient that held Europe spellbound. Marco Polo, with his account of China's bustling ports and populous cities and the wealth and might of the court of the 'Great Khan', whetted Europe's appetite and excited its avarice. Still hungry, miserable, and desolated by plague, early modern Europe hungered for a world wealthier and more splendid than its cold and shivering self.

Early European navigators and adventurers seemed to find ample confirmation for their dreams and expectations. Columbus was disappointed in not finding Cathay on the far Atlantic shore, but those who came after him soon rejoiced in their discovery of the American bonanza. The Spanish conquered and pillaged the golden empires of the Aztecs and the Incas, and then, their greed still unsatiated, they plundered the silver mines of Potosi and Zacatecas. The Portuguese and their successors in Africa found wealth in slaves, in ivory, in the gold of the Upper Niger and Monomatapa. Travellers in sixteenth- and seventeenth-century India were impressed by the thriving market towns they saw and amazed by the artistry and opulence of the Mughal court. The Frenchman François Bernier, in India between 1656 and 1668, remarked upon the great fertility and agricultural prosperity of Bengal and noted its flourishing trades in sugar and rice. China, too, seemed to fulfil even the high expectations Polo's *Travels* had aroused, and European observers of the sixteenth and seventeenth centuries were unanimous about the country's great productiveness. A

Portuguese Dominican friar summed up the general impression when he reported in 1556 that there existed in China the 'great abundance of all things necessary for food and for sustaining life'. The Jesuits went further and lauded Confucian civilization and presented to a credulous Europe its scholar officials as Platonic guardians, models of bureaucratic efficiency and paternalistic authority worthy of emulation by the Christian West.

While the most accessible wealth of the Aztecs and Incas was soon plundered and their artefacts melted down to satisfy Europe's lust for gold and silver, the civilizations of the East left a more durable impression. They set standards of craftsmanship and style which it took the West centuries to surpass, and produced goods that repeatedly shaped and influenced Europe's own fashions - China's delicate silks and porcelains, India's stunning chintzes, the lacquerware and wood-block prints of Japan. It took an industrial revolution in the West to supersede the artistry of the Orient, and even then in its willow-pattern plates and paisley-patterned shawls, its Axminster carpets, cheap printed cottons and floral wallpapers, the echoes of the Orient lived on.

And yet by a savage paradox the very lands that the adventurers of Henry the Navigator, Isabella of Castile and Elizabeth of England had so admired or lusted after, had, by the heyday of western imperialism, become synonymous with poverty and famine. Mexico by the late nineteenth century had become the United States' poor and shabby neighbour. Central America was in rapid transit from the lure of El Dorado to the home of banana republics. India under British rule knew famine after famine. Even Bengal, whose trading wealth and royal revenues had once tempted Robert Clive to 'shake the pagoda tree', had by 1914 a haggard, half-famished look. China, the very epitome of Marco Polo's miraculous East, had by the end of the nineteenth century sunk to being a byword for poverty and 'insufferable wretchedness'. The American writer W. H. Mallory summed up the western view of early twentieth-century China in a single damning phrase when he called it simply 'the land of famine'.

Since 1914 many things have changed. India's independence in 1947 and the Communist revolution in China in 1949 have helped to free those countries, in part, from the legacy of a famine past. But, for all that, to many Westerners India remains indelibly associated with beggary and semi-starvation - perhaps with justification since 200 million Indians live in 'abject poverty'. Latin America still speaks of hunger, as much these days through its shanty-towns and slums as through its peasant poor and hungry backlands. But it is Africa that is now most frequently depicted as the home of hunger. Ethiopia, Somalia, the Sahel, Mozambique – famine seems to rule the continent.

How did this devastating transformation from riches to rags come about? It might, of course, be that the change is more apparent than real, and that the actuality of these lands and peoples was always at variance with the European dream. Perhaps the wealth the early traders and adventurers saw, or thought they saw, was only the gilding on the dome, the thin skin of affluence on a society already poor and often hungry. Perhaps, but it is at least as likely that the advent of the West – the 'triumph of the West' as some of our more Euro-centric historians would have it – brought about changes that were so momentous that they threw indigenous economies and societies into disarray and made famine even more frequent and deadly than in the pre-European past.

Conquest and colonialism

Almost everywhere in the wider world Europe announced its arrival with famine and disease. In some areas of the globe it was conquest itself that wrought human destruction, less through the casualties that resulted from European arms on battlefields and in skirmishes than through the devastation caused by foraging troops and the confiscation of indigenous food stocks. In the Yucatan of Central America in the early sixteenth century the Maya, accustomed to fighting only when their food supplies had first been assured, found themselves at war with Spanish conquistadores who recognized no such rules of engagement and who plundered and pillaged alike at harvest-time and at planting. A brief drought, and conquest for the Maya became famine.

So did it, too, when a deceptive interlude of apparent submission after European annexation in Africa or Asia was followed by indigenous resistance movements and open warfare against the new rulers. In German East Africa the military campaigning of the 1890s was in itself disruptive of local agricultural production, but when in 1905–06 the southern provinces erupted in the Maji-Maji revolt the Germans retaliated not just with machine-guns and rifles against their barely armed adversaries but also with a 'scorched earth' policy that destroyed the crops and food reserves of hundreds of villages. Starvation quickly followed, but only to be treated by the colonial regime as a necessary part of the 'pacification' process. Having scarcely recovered from this ordeal, the region fell prey to famine again at the end of the First World War. Rival British and German forces had marched through the area several times during the war, living off the land and forcibly conscripting porters from the peasantry. The establishment of European control and the resolution of Europe's internecine struggles cost the rest of the world a terrible price. It was a price, moreover, that indigenous peoples were given no option about paying.

At times it was the unintended and uncontrollable inroads of disease that caused the greatest destruction. Epidemic diseases – smallpox, measles, and influenza among them – caused a demographic collapse in regions like Central America, the southern tip of Africa, Australasia and the islands of the Pacific where European diseases had been hitherto unknown. While the Europeans themselves remained largely immune to such afflictions, having gathered protection in their childhood or in their genes, the social cohesion and political resistance of indigenous peoples was fatally undermined. 'Wherever the European has trod', Charles Darwin commented, 'death seems to pursue the aboriginal. We may look to the wide extent of the Americas, Polynesia, the Cape of Good Hope and Australia, and we find the same result.'

Nor was this all. Such 'virgin soil' epidemics at times raged so widely and so violently that they incapacitated even where they did not kill. The local population could no longer feed itself or find the energy to plant and harvest its crops. In some instances, too, the dual invasion of the European and his diseases made white settlement easier, and what began as an epidemiological accident became part of an unfolding imperial design. Europeans, of course, were seldom the masters of the diseases they inadvertently introduced. In the West Indies and Central America, for example, the yellow fever which migrated with the slave trade from West Africa, became by the eighteenth and nineteenth centuries a serious hindrance to European settlement and control. But at the Cape, in Kenya, in New Zealand and across the broad expanse of North America, indigenous peoples lost access to, or control over, some of the world's most bounteous agricultural and grazing land, land that was able not only to feed the white settlers themselves but also to provide the beef, the wheat and wool for the growing millions in Europe. Those indigenes who survived conquest and disease were driven off their one-time pastures, hunting grounds and croplands. Many were confined to reservations too small, too arid, too stony, too disease-ridden, to support them. For them, too, conquest spelled hunger and, periodically, starvation.

Elsewhere destruction came through the consequences of trade. In

Asia in particular, where disease environments were significantly less favourable to European ascendency and where, for several centuries, military superiority lay in the balance, it was often through trade and other forms of economic intervention that Europe's disruptive influence began to be felt. Britain's opium trade with China, brushing aside the protests and prohibitions of the Chinese court, sparked the Opium War of 1839 and bundled the Celestial Empire down the slippery slope of imperial decline, into poverty, decay and drug addiction on a scale almost incomprehensible today. A society so weakened was not only less able to resist further western (and later Japanese) encroachment. Opium also undermined China's economic capacity and the self-sufficiency which had once encouraged it to spurn commercial overtures from the West. The flooding of India with the textiles of Lancashire reversed the once-thriving trade in chintzes and muslins and, though historians these days are rather more sceptical than the Drain Theoryists of a century ago about the degree of economic hardships that resulted, there seem grounds for arguing that this deprived a sizeable number of weavers, spinners and dyers of their living and increased the pressure on the land.

In India, too, once British rule had been firmly installed, economic changes were introduced which had a direct bearing, if not upon the actual causation of famines, then upon their immediate impact. In coastal Orissa, for example, the salt works around Chilka Lake were closed shortly before the famine of 1866 in order to further the interests of Britain's salt producers and traders. Villages hitherto reliant upon salt manufacture for their employment and income were among those most rapidly and adversely affected by the food shortages and famine that followed the failure of the monsoons.

Foreign production and trade in opium, textiles and salt alike undermined local productivity and employment and drew India, even China (though never subject to formal colonial rule), into an international economy under European control. In the long term imperial intervention might do something to redress the imbalance by providing, as in India, an infrastructure of roads and railways that could aid the growth of India's own commerce and industry and facilitate the movement of foodgrains in times of dearth as well as plenty. But these benefits were seldom unqualified. The railways, for example, discouraged the traditional practice of keeping reserves of grain as protection against harvest failures, and they made peasants perilously dependent upon the vagaries of a capricious international commodity market. Frequently the destructive consequences of western intervention were felt long before any benefits began to accrue to local capitalists and consumers. In itself growing rich, Europe had an unwholesome knack of making others poor and hungry.

In many parts of Africa colonial policies and practices disrupted existing systems of pastoralism and agriculture. Under the compulsion of colonial head and hut taxes, male labour was diverted into mines, plantations and urban employment. Subsistence agriculture, already in many parts of Black Africa mainly in the hands of women, was further devalued and starved of resources. Such educational and health facilities as colonial administrations provided were directed to the male workforce in the colonial-run sectors of the economy. As a poor and neglected section of the population female subsistence farmers and their children were particularly vulnerable when drought and epidemics struck.

The pressures of colonial taxation also drove peasants to cultivate areas formerly used only for grazing or for shifting cultivation which allowed the recovery of soil fertility without the permanent destruction of the natural groundcover. Through intensive working and the neglect of fallowing, such areas began to lose their productiveness or became scarred by soil erosion. Unfamiliar with tropical soils and climates, and convinced of the superiority of their own farming traditions, Europeans failed to recognize the ecological suitability of many indigenous techniques of cultivation and land-use. By denying Africans access to firearms and prohibiting game hunting except for whites, they further constricted the range of nutritional foodstuffs available to the indigenous population, especially in times of drought when other food sources failed. Although Africa, like Asia and Europe, certainly stood to benefit from the introduction of American food crops - in Africa's case principally maize and manioc - and though these became significant checks against famine starvation, they frequently resulted in dependence on a single staple (thus exposing the population to diseases caused by nutritional deficiency) while much valuable land was transferred from subsistence agriculture to the growing of cash crops and plantation products.

In some areas of Africa early colonial rule resulted in heavy depopulation. In the absence of detailed censuses for the early period, the extent of this demographic loss can never be fully ascertained, but the population of French Equatorial Africa, put at 15 million in 1900, had fallen to 10 million by 1914, and sank still further to 3 million by the census of 1921. Famine and related diseases were important causes of this immense human wastage. The population was worn out and worn away by forced labour, by military requisitioning and conscription, and by the interruption to family life caused by periods of prolonged and enforced separation. An official report of 1919 acknowledged, 'The native dies, primarily, because he lacks food. Famine is the principal cause of the depopulation of the Congo'. Military conscription and the diversion of labour from food production were similarly identified as contributing to famine in Gabon in 1924–26 and Niger in 1931.

At a time when Europe was fast making its own peasantries redundant, similar systems of agricultural exploitation and control were being devised or elaborated overseas. The peasants of Africa, Latin America and Asia laboured, however, not for their own subsistence, or even to supply purely local markets, but to satisfy the demands of the international economy. The negative consequences of this involvement in a market over which they had no control was made evident in many aspects of Third World peasant life, for example in the increasing disparity between the value of the peasants' crops and the price of the essential items of food and clothing they had to buy. Peasants in Senegal grew groundnuts for export, and thus contributed through their labour to the profitability of French possessions in West Africa. But the rice that formed the main item of their diet was imported from French Indo-China. As the controllers of the rice trade the French profited at both ends, buying cheap and selling dear, while the Senegalese found they had to grow more and more groundnuts simply in order to keep pace with the rising price of rice. In the 1920s the French authorities in Africa became alarmed at the wasting away of the indigenous workforce, for without 'human capital' the agricultural wealth of the region could not be tapped. As a result, there was increased provision for medical health care, albeit of a fairly rudimentary kind, but there was no fundamental change in the exploitative nature of the colonial economy.

During the world-wide Depression of the 1930s Britain and France defended their own economies from greater collapse by transferring part of the burden of economic recession to their territories overseas, especially in Africa. They reduced the prices paid for agricultural and other primary products while trying to maintain the cost of their own exports. Europe's continuing capacity to feed itself and to sustain its own prosperity was achieved at the expense of hardship and hunger in the colonial world.

It is striking how frequently colonial officials were either ignorant of, or insensitive to, the conditions of the people over whom they ruled. If the Indian Famine Code stands as testimony to a growing, if reluctant, acceptance of state responsibility for famine control and relief in one part of the colonial world, in many others neglect, indifference, even what Ambirajan calls 'a certain callousness towards life', seem to have been more characteristic and enduring attitudes. At times colonial neglect simply reflected the ill-informed nature of the administration, especially in the early years of foreign rule, or the assumption that the people would somehow, even in a famine, find food for themselves. Polly Hill cites the case of two famines in northern Nigeria, admittedly an area of 'indirect rule', in the first decade of the twentieth century. On the first occasion the colonial administration knew about the famine but London directed that relief should not be given. On the second, in 1908, no appeal was even made to the Colonial Office as the administration in Lagos apparently knew nothing of the famine until it read about it in an annual report. When asked about the episode the Acting Resident for Kano replied that the mortality had been 'considerable' but, he hoped, 'not so great as the natives allege' as 'we had no remedy at the time and therefore as little was said about it as possible.'

Ignorance and indifference were encouraged by the financial imperatives of the colonial regimes, loath to lessen their tax demand even in times of dearth and reluctant to provide relief measures that would cut too deeply into imperial revenues. The famine in the French colony of Niger in West Africa in 1931 offers one illustration of this. The immediate cause of the famine lay in deficient rainfall followed by a plague of locusts. French officials characteristically blamed African 'idleness', 'apathy' and 'fatalism' when, in fact, the peasants tried several times to plant fresh crops without any success. The harvest of the previous year, 1930, had given the peasants little security against their losses because of the high and inflexible nature of the colonial tax demand. Even during the famine grain continued to be levied from the worst-affected areas because officials refused to admit there was a shortfall. Taxes on animals further increased the peasant burden and were not reduced even though the real value of the animals and their products had fallen dramatically following the slump in world prices. For colonial officials who seldom ventured beyond the motor roads it was perhaps difficult, anyway, to appreciate the severity of the drought or to assess the extent of crop losses until the famine had already reached an advanced state. No official recognition of the famine was given until May 1931 when peasants had already begun to search for famine foods, cutting down palm trees to extract 'palm cabbage' and digging up lily roots from ditches and ponds. Even then, despite the reports that were beginning to reach him, the Governor of Niger turned a blind eye to mounting distress and continued to demand full taxes from the peasants. He, after all, was under pressure from metropolitan France, which was facing severe economic difficulties of its own, to maintain colonial revenues. The government made only minor concessions: prison rations were reduced, exports of millet were banned, and some food was distributed in the worst-hit areas. But otherwise the people of Niger were left to survive as best they could.

Masters and subjects

The great expansion of European empires of the late nineteenth century came at a time when mass starvation was already becoming an increasingly distant memory in Europe. Even the Irish famine of the 1840s was viewed by many commentators at the time as an anomaly and an anachronism, brought about by the peculiar conjunction of Irish backwardness and the potato blight. To Lord John Russell, the Prime Minister of the day, the famine did not seem to belong to the modern age at all: 'indeed' he remarked in January 1847, 'I should say it is like a famine of the 13th century acting upon a population of the 19th'. Nor did the fact that Russia remained so famine-prone greatly dent Europe's confidence in its capacity to feed itself: it was seen as yet another mark of the Asiatic barbarity and backwardness of the empire of the Tsars. Thus the persistence, even the proliferation, of famine in other parts of the globe, at a time when western Europe seemed to have successfully freed itself from hunger, profoundly influenced Europe's outlook on the rest of the world, nurturing a belief in its innate superiority over those countries and races which still remained subject to famine.

In seeking to understand the importance of this revolution in attitudes we cannot do better than to begin again with Malthus. Malthus's work is invariably taken as presenting a universal law in which the growth of population inevitably conflicts with society's inflexible food-producing capacity. But a closer reading will show his *Essay on the Principle of Population* to be significantly more than that. Le Roy Ladurie dubs him 'a prophet of the past' and, in view of Malthus's failure to foresee the potential growth of modern agriculture and industry, this is a valid description. But in his representation of what we would now call the Third World, Malthus was articulating the sentiments of the age of imperialism about to be born and helping to lay the basis for a view of the non-European world that has persisted ever since.

In addition to the examples which he took, predictably enough for an eighteenth-century scholar, from the history of classical Greece and Rome, Malthus also drew extensively from what was becoming known about the rest of the world in his day. Indeed, he was writing at a time when Europe was beginning to receive an unprecedented volume of information and opinion about the rest of mankind, partly as a result of which (and partly because of the dynamic changes affecting Europe's economy and society from within) Europeans were developing a keener sense of what distinguished them from other inhabitants of the planet. In addition to what he could learn from Gibbon about the decline and fall of ancient Rome, Malthus in the 1790s could quote from the recently published travels of James Bruce in Ethiopia and Mungo Park in West Africa, the voyages of Captain James Cook to Australia and New Zealand, and from the Orientalist scholar Sir William Jones and his translations of Hindu scriptures, like the Laws of Manu, previously unknown to the western world. Malthus thus felt himself equipped to comment upon the whole of humankind and not just upon its European segment.

For Malthus, unlike Montesquieu fifty years earlier, climate was not in itself a factor of much significance in explaining why one race or nation fared so differently from another. Instead, ranging widely across the globe and throughout human history, he identified a progression from the 'savages' of South America, Australia and Africa, to the more developed civilizations of Turkey, India and China, and on, (as befitted a man with a classical education) via Greece and Rome, to the western Europe of his own day. What for Malthus marked out the successive stages of this ascent from primitiveness to civilization was a transition from indolence to industry, from privation to property, from hunger to relative freedom from want. Montaigne and Rousseau had imagined man living outside civilized society, in the jungles of Brazil or in the North American wilderness, as enjoying a simplicity and contentment that might rival, even surpass, civilization's artificial attainments and vexatious constraints. Malthus, by contrast, saw no 'noble savages', only primitive creatures, ruled by nature and racked by starvation.

Everywhere, Malthus believed, the relationship between subsistence and population was the critical variable in dividing civilization from savagery. He concluded that most of the world remained subject to subsistence's cruel constraints or could only find crude and inhumane ways, like infanticide and abortion, of keeping births in line with food production. Most of the world, in his day as in the past, was governed by the iron hand of famine. Only Europe, and especially Britain (the

Irish aberration aside), stood out in his account as possessing the prudence and foresight to limit population by voluntary means. Although his point of departure might be the threat, as he saw it, of mass pauperism in England, he was also suggesting that Europe, by virtue of its control over excessive population growth, had the power to free itself from the 'positive checks' of famine and disease. Viewed in this light, the *Essay on the Principle of Population* was nothing less than a denunciation of 'man in a state of nature' and a paean in praise of Europe's growing mastery over hunger and want.

It was a startling and apparently illuminating contrast between two worlds – one hungry and one wise – and subsequent generations either took it up with alacrity or quickly arrived at identical conclusions. Charles Darwin, marrying what he read in Malthus with what he had observed from *The Beagle*, endorsed and extended the Malthusian hypothesis. The prolificacy of plants and animals, like that of Malthusian man, was held in check only by the want of sufficient food to sustain them all. This, wrote Darwin in *The Origin of Species*, was 'the doctrine of Malthus applied with manifold force to the whole animal and vegetable kingdoms', but with the added constraint that in these domains there could 'be no artificial increase of food, and no prudential restraint from marriage'. But Darwin, especially in *The Descent of Man* published twelve years later in 1871, saw important implications in this Malthusian 'struggle for existence' for mankind as well. Among 'civilized nations' the primary solution, he remarked, echoing Malthus, lay in 'restraining marriages'. But among 'savages', all tribes periodically suffered from severe famines and could only respond to 'the difficulty, or rather the impossibility of supporting all the infants that are born' by recourse to abortion and infanticide. Famine and its consequences were once more endorsed as a sign of savagery and the subordination of 'primitive man' to nature.

Later writers and imperial ideologues pursued the analogy between man and 'the animal kingdom' even further than Darwin had done. In the imperialism of the late nineteenth century the 'struggle for existence' and the 'survival of the fittest' were understood also to constitute the law of the human jungle, with race pitted against race in the struggle for mastery over land, food and other finite resources. Those best able to satisfy their own subsistence needs, by, for example, extending their empires into Asia and Africa or by peopling the Americas and Australasia, were accordingly those thought best able to survive and flourish on a crowded and competitive planet.

As famine departed from Europe's shores and disappeared into banishment abroad, so European attitudes towards it underwent a marked transformation. With growing technological powers at their command, rapidly expanding material resources, and a more assured food supply than previous generations had ever known, Europeans now felt themselves to be the masters of famine. Not only were irrigation systems developed, as in India, to reduce the hazards of drought and to boost agricultural productivity, not only were railways built to ease the rapid transportation of foodstuffs in times of dearth. Advances in medical science held out the prospect of containing the deadly diseases that had once marched shoulder to shoulder with famine. Identifying a link between deforestation and declining rainfall, forest departments were set up in India to conserve woodlands and preserve water supplies. No longer God's will, famine was now man's work, a challenge to be overcome through human industry and ingenuity, not met with superstition and fatalism.

Relegated to Europe's past, famine became a milestone marking the progression from the dark ages of hunger to the new era of world-wide trade and industry, technological achievement and environmental control. The Victorian historian, H. T. Buckle, gave confident expression to this sentiment when he wrote in his *History of Civilization in England* in 1885[1]:

> Those frightful famines, by which Europe used to be ravaged several times in every century, have ceased; and so successfully have we grappled with them, that there is not the slightest fear of their ever returning with anything like their former severity. Indeed, our resources are now so great, that we could at worst, only suffer from a slight and temporary scarcity . . .

Even the Irish famine of forty years earlier could be dismissed by Buckle as 'an exception'. 'It could', he wrote, 'have been easily baffled except for the poverty of the people, which frustrated our efforts to reduce it to a dearth'.

Europe's escape from famine favoured the rise of a new view of nature as something that could be aesthetically pleasing, a welcome contrast to factory chimneys and sprawling cities. Nature was no longer as frustrating, as life-drainingly niggardly, as it had been when so many lives depended upon winning subsistence from the soil. Would Wordsworth, one wonders, have found in the English Lakeland echoes of a 'blissful Eden' and the 'beauteous forms of nature' if he had known it two centuries earlier, as Andrew Appleby describes it, subject to repeated visitations of famine and epidemic

1. *History of Civilization in England*, p. 155.

typhus? Europe could wax lyrical about landscapes now that it was no longer so exclusively dependent upon the land for its food.

The more Europe's wealth, trade and industry grew, the less it felt climate to be a vital determinant – at least of its own history, for in their backwardness other continents remained nature's captives. After a lengthy review of how climate, soil and natural disasters adversely affected other regions of the globe, Buckle continued:

> But, in Europe, the determining cause is not so much these physical peculiarities, as the skill and energy of man. Formerly the richest countries were those in which nature was most bountiful; now the richest countries are those in which man is most active. For, in our age of the world, if nature is parsimonious, we know how to compensate for her deficiencies . . . From these facts in may be fairly inferred that the advance of European civilization is characterized by a diminishing influence of physical laws, and on increasing influence of mental laws.[2]

Overlooking the possibility that they, by the very manner of their intervention and rule, might themselves have caused or contributed to others' sickness and hunger, Europeans instead saw the famines they encountered in distant parts of the world as a sign of the inferiority of the inhabitants and of their apathy in the face of an adversary over which Europe had long since triumphed. Just as trade and technology became the twin panaceas of the Victorian age, so hunger became an imperial stereotype of non-European peoples. It formed a central part of the representation of that 'other' which stood in contradistinction to Europe's dynamic energy and increasing mastery over nature.

Where once the Orient spoke of opulence now it told only of hunger. Famine became, in the West's perception, almost the normal state of all societies other than its own. The destitution that famine engendered, the exhaustion, the lethargy and the dependence that it bred, were seen as representative of Asian or African societies as a whole. Hence, China (or India or some forlorn region of Africa) could be branded 'the land of famine' as if that summed up all that needed to be understood about it. It was perhaps in this sense more than any other that famine became the great leveller, for it reduced all non-white societies, in the European estimation, to a common zero. Where in Malthus there had been a lingering respect for the civilizations of the East (as seen through the admiring eyes of Orientalist scholars and Jesuit emissaries), even a few decades later that too had vanished. Of what value, it might be asked, were the laws of Manu or the

2. *History of Civilization in England*, p. 156.

pretentions of mandarins if they could do nothing to save India or China from want and famine? In praising its own practicality and ingenuity, Europe denigrated and despised those civilizations in which hunger still reigned.

This interpretation of famine's significance was clearly evident in India. There the stereotype of Indian inertia in the face of famine was not only commonplace in itself; it was also taken to endorse other assumptions about Indian, especially Hindu, fatalism and super-stition. In the course of a discussion of famine in India, an anony-mous writer in the *Edinburgh Review* in 1877 passed from criticizing peasant apathy to condemnation of the Hindu caste system. To many nineteenth-century European observers caste meant obscurantism and intransigence: it was the main obstruction to the spread of progress and reform. Perhaps not surprisingly, therefore, caste 'prejudice' could also be called the 'great ally of famine' and 'the great minister of death', because, the writer claimed, it prevented people from leaving their homes and quitting their hereditary occupations to search for work and eat the food a benevolent administration provided for them in its relief camps. Such, according to the author, was the apathy and 'the profound melancholy caused by famine' that Europeans had almost to force food 'down the throats of a passively starving people'. Food and medicine were only provided for the poor when Europeans took the initiative, and then, once Britons had set Indians to work, 'the effect . . . was almost magical'.

This perceived contrast between the dynamism of the white man and the apathy of the 'native' found fictional form in Rudyard Kipling's story 'William the Conqueror'. Like so much of his writing, this is not only a vividly evocative tale of British India; it is also richly emblematic of empire. Apart from a Muslim servant, Indians appear in it only as victims – as 'wailing, walking skeletons', or as the 'phantoms of babies' which starving mothers thrust into the care of European officials. The model for the heroine of the title, the sister of a Punjab police officer, may (as Angus Wilson suggests) have been an American woman Kipling knew, but, by casting a woman alongside a man (Scott) as the central characters of the story, Kipling was doing more than simply spicing it with romantic interest. He was also, perhaps unconsciously, echoing the Indian concept of benevolent authority as *ma-bap* ('mother-father'). Scott and William hit upon the idea of feeding imported wheat, which the famine-stricken south Indians, as rice-eaters, are loath to touch, to goats which can then be milked to keep the famished children alive. Thus the famine is more than just a backcloth to the unfolding love story of William and Scott.

It serves to exemplify, even to glorify, the ingenuity and dedication of the ruling race and it paints a vivid contrast between European energy and the apparent helplessness of the starving villagers. The title of the story not only celebrates William's romantic triumph but also identifies British dominion in India with the vigour and achievement of the Norman conquest in England eight centuries earlier. With *laissez-faire* for the moment put aside, the conquest of famine becomes paradigmatic of imperial purpose and a legitimation for white rule over black. Indeed, it was shortly after he wrote 'William the Conqueror' in the mid-1890s that Kipling penned the lines:

> Take up the White Man's burden,
> The savage wars of peace –
> Fill full the mouth of Famine,
> And bid the sickness cease.

Although the white man's conquest of famine was for Kipling essentially a secular task, it also acquired a powerful evangelical significance. In China, where imperial rule had not formally intruded, famine relief, along with the provision of medical services and training, was one of the principal ways in which Christianity was propagated. In the late nineteenth century missionaries identified themselves with western science and technology, seeing in them unequivocal evidence of the superiority of the West, of Christian care and capability over the cruelty and indifference to human suffering they believed to be inherent in indigenous systems of belief. Timothy Richard of the Baptist Missionary Society reflected Europe's confidence in its mastery over nature when he wrote:

In pondering Western civilization, I felt that its advantage over Chinese civilization was due to the fact that it sought to discover the workings of God in Nature, and to apply the laws of Nature for the service of mankind. This was in obedience to God's command to Adam to have dominion over all things. In applying the laws of science to the needs of man, Western nations had made marvellous inventions that were little less wonderful than miracles.[3]

Richard saw in the North China famine of 1876–79 an opportunity sent by God to overcome Chinese resistance to the Gospel and win converts through a practical demonstration of Christian concern. Rice might triumph where previously rhetoric had failed. Richard had been in Shantung since 1870 and, like many missionaries in China at the

3. Quoted in Paul Richard Bohr, *Famine in China and the Missionary*, p. 146.

time, he had begun by 'seeking the worthy' - the Confucian gentry. But at their hands he had met with only uninterest and disdain. In turning to the poor and the peasants during the famine he was acknowledging the failure of this elite strategy and, like many other missionaries in Asia and Africa at about the same time, was turning to an attempt to win over the mass of the people instead.

Famine relief activities of the kind Richard pioneered in China were not without their negative repercussions. Chinese gentry and officials, like many high-caste Hindus in India, were alarmed to find the missionaries 'stealing the hearts of the people' and creating 'rice Christians'. The founding of orphanages for children abandoned or left homeless during times of famine was particularly disliked, and there were allegations that the missionaries had kidnapped the children or were immorally exploiting their distress to indoctrinate and convert them. For all their expectations of assistance many peasants in India and China were deeply suspicious of the motives behind the establishment of relief camps and soup kitchens, whether organized by missionary societies or, as in India, by the colonial state itself. Rumours circulated of forced conversion to Christianity or compulsory enlistment as coolies to serve in some foreign land. The heavy mortality in relief centres in India encouraged a belief that the British were poisoning off a population which had grown too large and restive. The manner and, still more, the perception of western intervention might thus produce the opposite effect to that the missionaries and administrators expected and in some places it led to a strengthening of anti-missionary and anti-western sentiment. But even that negative reaction could be seen by westerners as confirmation of the childish superstition and rank ingratitude of those they were trying to help.

Thus for Richard and many other missionaries famine relief work remained an ideal evangelical method, opening up direct contact with the people and providing an opportunity to demonstrate practical concern for the poor and needy. He believed that the knowledge 'that I was distributing relief to the famine sufferer was convincing proof to the multitudes that my religion was good'. He hoped to present Christianity 'in such a way that it would commend itself to the conscience of the Chinese as superior to anything they themselves possessed'. His friend and colleague, John Nevis, believed that famine relief work was indeed as effective as Richard claimed and had 'a strong influence in removing prejudices and preparing the way for the reception of Christianity' in China. M. Geraldine Guinness in her *Story of the China Inland Mission*, published in 1893-94, similarly maintained that the missionary influence acquired during 'those years of terrible distress' in the late 1870s 'was never lost. Shansi was opened to the Gospel from end to end . . .'

The politics of famine relief

The use of famine in China and India to demonstrate European superiority over man and nature was itself only part of the changing significance famine held for the western world. Nineteenth-century advances in transport and communications and the spead of imperial dominion and trade enabled news of distant famines to be relayed rapidly to western audiences. They also provided the means by which western wealth could be in some small measure be channelled back to the lands from which it had been plundered. Modern means of transport and communication made possible the organization of international relief funds to distribute food, money and clothing on the opposite side of the globe. These undoubtedly contributed to the relief of much human suffering, but in making their appeals to western donors they projected a one-dimensional image of famine 'victims' (or 'subjects' as they were sometimes called). The apparent contrast between European dynamism and 'native' apathy already established in the imperial mind and the sense of western power and superiority that famine in the Third World was increasingly coming to signify were thereby further reinforced.

Such a representation gained impetus from the increasing volume of correspondence and reports – from travellers, journalists, officials, missionaries and others – that poured into the literate capitals of the western world during the imperial age. A Europe which had once known of other people's famines only as a distant echo of its own, could now read up-to-date reports of famine in far-away China or India. Appeals in newspapers, in books and through lantern-slide lectures were powerfully supported by line-drawings and photographs which graphically portrayed famine's misery the better to provoke pity and elicit a charitable response. One has only to look at late nineteenth-century photographs of famine to see images of hunger which reduced those exposed to the camera's cruel gaze to the status of sub-human specimens – the emaciated limbs and protruding bones, the women's bared and withered breasts, the lolling heads and swollen bellies of the starving children – stripped of any last vestige of dignity and individuality, robbed even of the privacy of their grief and anguish, represented solely as 'victims' whose appearance said nothing of determination and struggle but told only of helplessness and a tragic submission to inertia and want.

The growing awareness of famine abroad led directly to international measures for its amelioration. Appeals were launched across Europe and North America to raise funds for the starving. Agencies were established to distribute food, money and other essentials half way across the world. Ireland's 'Great Hunger' in the 1840s inspired one of the first examples of the international mobilization of famine relief – with donations coming not only from Britain and other parts of Europe but also from the United States and even European residents in India. The famines of the 1860s and 1870s seem to have marked the first substantial efforts to organize famine relief for Asia. Funds were organized from the Mansion House in London for this purpose and raised several million pounds to send to India, China and Persia. In China between 1876 and 1879 Timothy Richard not only organized relief activities in the hard-hit provinces of Shantung and Shansi but also sought the assistance of the country's foreign residents through the China Famine Relief Fund set up in Shanghai in January 1878. It issued a direct appeal for support to England and the United States which ran: 'Appalling famine raging throughout North China. Nine million people reported destitute. Children daily sold in markets for food.' A London Committee was established, and by September 1878 when subscriptions closed £32,303 had been raised. A further £60,000 was collected through a Mansion House Fund set up under the Lord Mayor of London and Archbishop of Canterbury in March 1878. At about the same time, £500,000 was collected in Britain for famine-stricken South India.

That these relief funds and the activities which they helped finance had more than a purely humanitarian purpose and appeal is evident from speeches and private observations made at the time. Although he was later made to retract (for fear that Indian sentiment would be offended by so explicit a declaration), in May 1861 the Lord Mayor of London, William Cubitt, said, in sending funds for famine relief to India, that he hoped they would

> lead to a consolidation of our power, and thus not only reconcile India to our control, but cause an improvement in the religious aspect of the country, and by the extension of the Christian religion conduce to the eternal happiness of the people.[4]

4. Quoted in B. M. Bhatia, *Famines in India*, 1967 edition, p. 63.

A British Consul writing at the time of the north China famine of 1876-79 also hinted at the wider imperial benefits that might accrue from the missionaries' relief activities when he remarked that 'The distribution of funds by the brave and judicious men engaged in the work will do more to open China to us than a dozen wars'.

By the early decades of the twentieth century relief was being organized for China on a massive scale. The China International Famine Relief Commission, formed in 1920, was mainly administered by missionaries who saw it as a 'ministry of loving deeds'. Special funds were raised in 1921, 1930 and 1935-6 to aid those affected by famines, floods and other disasters. After its activities during the 1920-21 famine CIFRC was left with some $2 million which it invested in projects – such as irrigation works, flood control schemes, and road construction – that would be of lasting value. Between 1922 and 1936 CIFRC spent $50 (Chinese) million and following the hunger and homelessness caused by the flooding of the Yangtse River in 1931, nearly half a million tons of wheat and flour were shipped to China from the United States. Gradually, however, the organizers began to realize the immensity of the task that confronted them and to see that China's poverty and hunger was a social and political problem and not simply a matter of providing relief.

However, India and China were not the only recipients of international famine relief, nor was religion its only inspiration. As international relief became a well-established part of the relationship between an affluent West and its less prosperous neighbours, so its economic and political value began to be exploited as well. The United States, grain rich and famine-free, with an agrarian economy increasingly dependent on finding outlets for its food surpluses overseas, imbued with a strong sense of its own dynamic energy and moral purpose, and without much of an empire of its own on which to lavish its attentions, played a critical role in expanding the political and economic possibilities of international famine relief.

Some assistance had been sent from the United States to Ireland at the time of the potato famine, but the key departure came with the 1891–92 famine in Russia when a total of $700,000 was raised and a considerable quantity of grain despatched. This was clearly meant as a humanitarian gesture, but it was not without other purposes and effects. The millers and farmers who took an active part in the fundraising campaign saw it as a way of breaking into the market of their main grain-producing rival. At a more general moral and political level, the very need to send relief to Russia was seen as an indication of the superiority of American enterprise and democracy over the poverty of the Russian people caused by their heartless and tyrannical Tsars. The editor of the *New York Times* commented in December 1891 that the failure of other countries to aid Russia was a 'melancholy illustration of the isolation of Russia from the civilized world' and 'one of the penalties Russia pays for her barbarism'.

The fall of the Tsars in 1917 brought neither an end to Russian hunger nor a lasting change in American perceptions of its significance. At the end of the First World War, as Russia and eastern Europe again fell prey to mass hunger, food and medical supplies were once more sent in to help the sufferers. Herbert Hoover, who had been in charge of the Commission for Relief in the Belgium campaign and overseen the distribution of 28 million metric tons of US grain in Europe during the First World War, helped to set up the American Relief Administration in 1919. As America's 'food czar' he saw the value of food relief in a war-torn and hungry Europe as a means of gaining political leverage in societies that were on the brink of revolution (or, like Russia, already in its throes). In name the cause was humanitarian, and on these grounds it was difficult for Russia's new rulers to refuse the charity Hoover held out to them. But the motivation behind it was frankly political. Hoover believed that, at a time when overt political intervention was largely impractical, 'humanitarian aid' would show the people of eastern Europe that America was concerned for their welfare and would feed them even if their own governments could not, or would not. In his account of Hoover's activities in Europe at this time, H. H. Fisher wrote:

> Every pound of flour, every tin of milk, every ounce of fat that he drove through the blockade into Germany or distributed in the newly formed states was a vastly more effective weapon against Bolshevism than the machine guns and tanks delivered to the counter-revolutionary armies of Russian Whites. But in this he was not denying to the harassed people the right to choose between a government of soviets and a democracy; he was fighting the real manifestations of Bolshevism, famine, bloodshed, chaos. To the bewildered people of Central Europe the emissaries of Bolshevism did not offer merely a new political system, but escape from the weight of misery piled up by the war. Thus Bolshevism prospered as starvation and despair spread; it halted when food came and hope revived.[5]

At times Hoover openly used food as a political weapon by threatening to cut off supplies of American wheat to governments whose policies he disliked. The communist regime of Bela Kun in Hungary

5. *The Famine in Soviet Russia, 1919-1923*, pp. 57-8.

was one casualty of his strategy in 1919. But in Russia, in order to allay Bolshevik suspicions, a more cautious approach was employed. Hoover's hopes of using American wheat and Russian hunger to overturn Bolshevism did not materialize, but there was perhaps some truth in Trotsky's remark that the world revolution failed because of the faith created by Hoover's food aid in the benevolence of the 'Uncle from America'.

The political utility of famine relief and food aid which Hoover so persuasively advocated during and immediately following the First World War was taken up again at the end of the second, when it was once more felt that by pumping money and grain into Europe part at least of the continent could be saved from the communist advance. In 1946-47 alone over 8.5 million tons of American grain were sent to forestall famine and revolution in Europe. Again a leading figure in the feeding of a needy Europe, Herbert Hoover admitted that while the 'major interest was relief of famine', the American government was also concerned about 'the forces moving in the world and their impact upon our country - and especially with the spread of Communism.' Feeding Europe and fighting famine on the other side of the Atlantic was one way of defending America from communist encirclement and attack.

But the United States' food aid was never just political in its motivation. Hoover was able to unite the requirements of American foreign policy with the needs of its own agrarian economy. After a peak of productivity and profitability in 1919 due to wartime demand and the weakness of its European competitors, the US economy began to falter. Wheat prices fell, threatening ruin to many thousands of grain producers. Hoover was able to help them and win support for his overseas aid programme. He ensured good prices and a continuing demand for the farmers' grain by selling off the surplus to feed the starving in Europe, and to pay for it he persuaded Congress to make a grant of $20 million in December 1921.

Since the Second World War the United States has continued to pursue the policies Hoover pioneered, withholding food assistance from countries like Marxist-run Ethiopia, of which it politically disapproves, and using food shipments to ensure the continued reliability and dependency of its allies, like Egypt since the Camp David agreement. During Richard Nixon's presidency the United States sent food to Cambodia and South Vietnam, underlining its commitment to those beleaguered regimes. Since the 1960s governing circles in America have freely equated food with power and given this doctrine an application far wider than even Herbert Hoover had envisaged. A secret report produced by the CIA in August 1974, and cited by Susan George, recognized that American abundance in a world of hunger 'could give the United States a measure of power it had never had before' and 'an economic and political dominance' greater even than that it had enjoyed in the immediate post-war years.

Alongside these political objectives and opportunities, continuing food aid and exports have helped to save American grain farmers from bankruptcy. Overseas aid has been vital to the United States economy as a safety valve for its domestic over-production. In 1961 the Kennedy administration was faced with the greatest American food surplus in history, and it was this domestic situation rather than humanitarian concern that prompted massive grain shipments overseas in the following years – notably in 1966 when one-fifth of the entire US wheat crop was sent to India to relieve the effects of famine in Bihar. The wheat farmers of the United States need a hungry world if they are to survive. Food aid accounted for 28 per cent of US overseas development assistance between 1946 and 1976. PL 480, the Agricultural Trade Development and Assistance Act of 1954, was debated and approved by Congress not for humanitarian reasons or for development ends but in order to promote trade and dispose of existing surpluses. Food aid has served to open up new markets for American farm products, especially in Africa and Asia, often to the detriment of local agriculture, and the threat of its withdrawal or denial has been used to put pressure on countries to accept other forms of American economic intervention and political control.

'Food is power'

Each generation rediscovers or reinterprets famine in the light of its own experiences, fears and expectations. Banished abroad by one generation, its imminent demise confidently proclaimed by a second, famine has returned to haunt a third in fantasy and dread, while a fourth has found famine suddenly staring it in the face. With Europe and the white man's world seemingly secured from hunger in the aftermath of the Second World War, famine has again been relegated, more emphatically than ever before, to the status of a Third World affliction. But even there it cannot be laid to rest.

At the same time that the United States was profiting economically and politically from world hunger, several American writers in the 1960s and 1970s began to argue that America could not continue indefinitely to provide the food needed by a rapidly growing global population and that it would need in future to confine its largesse to countries that were politically acceptable or seen to be making real progress in birth control. The combination of fear, anger, personal vulnerability and sheer incomprehension that lay behind the response to rapidly increasing Third World populations has already been suggested in an earlier chapter with Ehrlich's road-to-Damascus revelation in a Delhi taxi. In the same book, *The Population Bomb*, Ehrlich further revealed the political reasoning behind his deep alarm over Third World population growth and the famines he saw as inevitably arising out of it. He gives three 'scenarios' of the 'famine decades' to come, in each of which a food crisis in the Third World becomes the starting point for a social and political upheaval that rapidly threatens to engulf the United States. In the third of these famine fantasies, for example, the cutting off of American food aid causes food riots and mass starvation in several Asian countries and triggers the overthrow of their governments. Thereafter, Ehrlich continues, 'Most of the countries of Africa and South America slide backwards into famine and local warfare. Many adopt Communistic governments, but few are able to achieve any stability'. In the resulting global catastrophe 500 million people starve to death.

Other writers, like William and Paul Paddock and Garrett Hardin pursued their Malthusian nightmares still further. Despairing of speedy scientific and technological solutions to steepling population growth and near-stagnant food production in the Third World, they claimed that a point had already been reached at which the United States (along with other 'granary' states like Canada) had to make an apparently harsh but vital decision. In order to continue to feed its own people and to help the 'deserving poor' among its allies, America would have to cut off food aid to other hungry nations. This, in the brutal language of the battlefield hospital, was the process of 'triage', sorting out those who could be saved and the 'walking wounded' from the worst 'basket cases'. This, by another blunt analogy, was the logic of the overcrowded lifeboat: given finite resources, some of the weakest had to be sacrificed - or sacrifice themselves - in order that others might survive. As the Paddocks put it, after reflecting on the extraordinary productivity of American, as compared to Third World, agriculture, 'We do indeed have great power, but the hungry maw outside our borders is beyond the ability of even our abundance to satisfy'. It was America's food: therefore, America had the right and the obligation to decide how it was to be distributed among all the many hungry who craved and clamoured for it.

By arrogating to itself the right to decide who should live and who should die, who should be fed and who perish from starvation, the Paddocks and writers like them were inviting the United States to exercise an awesome and unprecedented power over the rest of the globe. To the theorists of 'triage' this was no more than the stark realities of the world's deteriorating food situation urgently dictated. But it could be understood, too, as the most expansive illustration ever offered of the way in which famine and the fear of famine have haunted human history throughout the ages and have continued to fashion the relations between rich and poor, between those who possess and control food and those who live and die in want.

Notes on Further Reading

General Works

Although the literature on famine is now vast and growing rapidly there have been disappointingly few books of a general interpretive nature. The subject has seemingly lent itself more to detailed monographs and papers than to broad comparative discussion. The exceptions are works by non-historians, though inevitably they draw heavily upon historical source materials and case studies.

Among the most helpful introductions to famine from a demographic standpoint are Michael W. Flinn, *The European Demographic System, 1500-1820* (1981), and D. B. Grigg, *Population Growth and Agrarian Change: An Historical Perspective* (1980), which examine Malthusian theory in the light of western European experience since the thirteenth century. A second study by David Grigg, *The World Food Problem, 1950-1980* (1985), provides a valuable contemporary perspective. The collection of essays *Hunger and History: The Impact of Changing Food Production and Consumption Patterns on Society* (1985), edited by Robert I. Rotberg and Theodore K. Rabb, brings together recent research on demography, nutrition and disease as well as famine. For a more technical (and especially nutritional) understanding of famine, see the volume edited by G. Blix, Y. Hofvander and B. Vahlquist, *Famine: A Symposium dealing with Nutrition and Relief Operations in Times of Disaster* (1971). Robert Dirks, 'Social Responses during Severe Food Shortages and Famine', *Current Anthropology*, 21, 1980, conveniently surveys the literature on famine behaviour and has an extensive bibliography.

Most studies of famine attempt to offer some definition of what is meant by the term. Frank A. Southard writing in the *Encyclopedia of the Social Sciences*, volume VI, in 1931, and M. K. Bennett, in the *International Encyclopedia of the Social Sciences*, volume 5, in 1968, provide useful brief discussions of the characteristics of famine. However, their definitions (and those of many other writers) linking famine directly with absolute food shortages need qualification in the light of Amartya Sen's *Poverty and Famines: An Essay on Entitlement and Deprivation* (1981), which has already become a classic in the literature on famine. Many recent books and articles have been further explorations and qualifications of his 'entitlements' thesis. Ajit Kumar Ghose, 'Food Supply and Starvation: A Study of Famines with Reference to the Indian Sub-Continent', *Oxford Economic Papers*, 34, 1982, is one such example.

Like economists, geographers have also made a number of important contributions to the recent literature on famine. Bruce Currey and Graeme Hugo (eds), *Famine as a Geographical Phenomenon* contains several interesting articles, especially on India. William A. Dando, *The Geography of Famine* (1980) is certainly far-ranging and helpful as background to the current situation but it fails to develop a convincing theory about the historical distribution of famines. From the climatic standpoint, there is Reid A. Bryson and Thomas J. Murray, *Climates of Hunger: Mankind and the World's Changing Weather* (1977), and H. H. Lamb, *Climate, History and the Modern World* (1982); but the shades of Ellsworth Huntington somehow live on in these works, and the historian might prefer to trust Emmanuel Le Roy Ladurie's adventurous sally into this field: *Times of Feast, Times of Famine: A History of Climate since the Year 1000* (1972).

Peasants have featured increasingly prominently in the debate about famine and its economic and political consequences. Eric R. Wolf's *Peasants* (1966) is useful as an introduction to the subject as a whole, while Clifford Geertz, *Agricultural Involution: The Process of Ecological Change in Indonesia* (1963) and David Ludden, *Peasant History in South India* (1985) are, in their very different ways, richly informative about peasant life and agriculture in Asia. Ronald E. Seavoy's *Famine in Peasant Societies* (1986) draws upon a vast array of material, but the central claim – that peasant societies have been governed by an 'indolence ethic' – remains a dubious proposition. More persuasive is James C. Scott's *The Moral Economy of the Peasant: Rebellion and Subsistence in Southeast Asia* (1976), which has stimulated a great deal of discussion about the nature of peasant economy, society and resistance. The 'moral economy' argument was earlier applied to the more specific context of urban food riots by E. P. Thompson in 'The Moral Economy of the English Crowd in the Eighteenth Century', *Past and Present*, 50, 1971. John Walter and Keith Wrightson, 'Dearth and Social Order in Early Modern England', *Past and Present*, 71, 1976, is an interesting corollary to the Thompson thesis, and food riots and their significance have been explored in a number of other regional studies, such as Louise A. Tilly, 'The Food Riot as a Form of Political Conflict in France', *Journal of Interdisciplinary History*, II,

1971; Charles Tilly, 'Food Supply and Public Order in Modern Europe', in *The Formation of National States in Western Europe* (1975), edited by Charles Tilly. The works of George Rudé, E. J. Hobsbawm and Richard Cobb provide many other examples for eighteenth and nineteenth century England and France. David Arnold, 'Looting, Grain Riots and Government Policy in South India, 1918', *Past and Present*, 84, 1979, is one of several attempts to examine the phenomenon further afield.

Reaching further back in the literature on famine, there are a number of works which have made an enduring contribution to the subject. Apart from Malthus's *An Essay on the Principle of Population*, itself the subject of a vast literature – see, for instance, Michael Turner (ed.), *Malthus and His Time* (1986) – a still stimulating point of departure is Cornelius Walford's *The Famines of the World: Past and Present*, presented as two papers to the Statistical Society of London in 1878–79 and published in book form in 1879. Walford's observation: 'I did not find that any previous writer has deemed the subject of famines worthy of careful investigation' is hardly accurate, but it does remind us how far the pursuit of famine has advanced over the past century or so. Among other earlier works deserving mention, Josué de Castro's *The Geopolitics of Hunger* (entitled *The Geography of Hunger* when first published in 1952) is a powerful polemic against man-made hunger. A stimulating book, full of interest and insight rather than a practical guide to the famine phenomenon, it makes curiously little distinction between famine and endemic hunger and malnutrition. A classic of a rather different kind is Ester Boserup *The Conditions of Economic Growth: The Economics of Agrarian Growth under Population Pressure* (1965). Although the author has since become rather more cautious in her arguments, (see *Women's Role in Economic Development* (1970) and *Population and Technology*, 1980) this pioneering work, however flawed it may be, remains of value for the boldness of its anti-Malthusianism. Mark Nathan Cohen's *The Food Crisis in Prehistory: Overpopulation and the Origins of Agriculture* (1977) is a fascinating attempt to extend the Boserup thesis back to a much earlier period.

Historical studies of famine

Much of the famine literature by and for historians has been confined to the study of specific famines and specific areas. Inevitably, it varies greatly in approach, argument and sophistication. Although there have been few monographs devoted to the subject of famine alone, dearth and hunger occur frequently in a vast range of historical writing on medieval and early modern Europe. Wilhelm Abel, *Agricultural Fluctuations in Europe from the Thirteenth to the Twentieth Centuries* (first published in German in 1935); Andrew A. Appleby, 'Epidemics and Famine in the Little Ice Age', *Journal of Interdisciplinary History*, X, 1980; B. H. Slicher van Bath, *The Agrarian History of Western Europe, A.D. 500-1850* (1963); Guy Bois, *The Crisis of Feudalism: Economy and Society in Eastern Normandy, c. 1300-1550* (1984); Georges Duby, *The Early Growth of the European Economy: Warriors and Peasants from the Seventh to the Twelfth Century* (1974) and *Rural Economy and Country Life in the Medieval West* (1976); Pierre Goubert, *Beauvais et le Beauvaisis de 1600 à 1730* (1960) and *The French Peasantry in the Seventeenth Century* (1982); Steven L. Kaplan, *Bread, Politics and Political Economy in the Reign of Louis XV* (1976); Ian Kershaw, 'The Great Famine and Agrarian Crisis in England, 1315-1322', *Past and Present*, 59, 1973; Emmanuel Le Roy Ladurie, *The Peasants of Languedoc* (1974); Henry S. Lucas, 'The Great European Famine of 1315, 1316, and 1317', *Speculum*, 5, 1930; John D. Post, *The Last Great Subsistence Crisis in the Western World* (1977); and M. M. Postan, *The Medieval Economy and Society* (1972), are among the most useful sources.

Famine has also, of course, figured centrally in many other historical debates, notably over the demographic and economic impact of the plague and other epidemic diseases. Two examples of this for England are Andrew A. Appleby, *Famine in Tudor and Stuart England* (1978), and John Hatcher, *Plague, Population and the English Economy, 1348-1530* (1977). Of particular interest, too, is the relationship with the Corn Laws and agricultural productivity in England: see Donald G. Barnes, *A History of the English Corn Laws from 1660-1846* (1930), and W. G. Hoskins, 'Harvest Fluctuations and English Economic History, 1480-1619', *Agricultural History Review*, XII, 1964, and 'Harvest Fluctuations and English Economic History, 1620-1759', *ibid.*, XVI, 1968, for examples of this.

In the literature on famine in Europe, two countries have received particular attention - Ireland and Russia. Cecil Woodham-Smith, *The Great Hunger: Ireland, 1845-1849* (1962) remains one of the most accessible and moving histories of any famine. It is ably supported by R. Dudley Edwards and T. Desmond Williams (eds) *The Great Famine: Studies in Irish History, 1845-52* (1957). But the causes and consequences of the 'Great Hunger' have remained a subject of scholarly controversy. K. H. Connell's article, 'The Potato in Ireland', *Past and*

Present, 23, 1962, has sparked much discussion about the potato's part in Ireland's eighteenth and nineteenth century population boom, while L. M. Cullen, 'Irish History without the Potato', *Past and Present*, 40, 1968; L. M. Cullen and F. Furet (eds), *Ireland and France 17th-20th Centuries: Towards a Comparative Study of Rural History* (1980); J. M. Goldstrom and L. A. Clarkson (eds), *Irish Population, Economy, and Society* (1981); and Joel Mokyr, *Why Ireland Starved: A Quantitative and Analytical History of the Irish Economy, 1800-1850* (1983), all contain noteworthy qualifications of the potato hypothesis. Other salient aspects of the Irish famine have been explored in, among other works, Michael Beames, *Peasants and Power: The Whiteboy Movements and their Control in Pre-Famine Ireland* (1983); R. D. Collinson Black, *Economic Thought and the Irish Question, 1817-1870* (1960); Daniel J. Casey and Robert E. Rhodes (eds), *Views of the Irish Peasantry* (1977); and F. S. L. Lyons, *Ireland since the Famine* (1971). There are fascinating parallels (and contrasts) between famine in Ireland and in western Scotland in the 1840s: these are explored in L. M. Cullen and T. C. Smout (eds), *Comparative Aspects of Scottish and Irish Economic and Social History, 1600-1900* (1977), and James Hunter, *The Making of the Crofting Community* (1976),

Russia's famines have been extensively reviewed and there exists a considerable literature in English. Richard Hellie, *Slavery in Russia, 1450-1725* (1982) offers evidence of food scarcity as a cause of voluntary slavery in early modern Russia; R. E. F. Smith, *Peasant Farming in Muscovy* (1977) provides the background to the Muscovy famine of 1601-3. The famines of the nineteenth and twentieth centuries are examined in Richard G. Robbins, *Famine in Russia, 1891-1892: The Imperial Government Responds to a Crisis* (1975); Geroid T. Robinson, *Rural Russia under the Old Regime* (1932); Dana G. Dalrymple, 'The Soviet Famine of 1932-34', *Soviet Studies*, 15, 1964; Moshe Lewin, ' "Taking Grain": Soviet Policies of Agricultural Procurement before the War', in C. Abramsky (ed.), *Essays in Honour of E. H. Carr* (1974); and there is Malcolm Muggeridge's caustic view in *Winter in Moscow* (1934).

Looking beyond the shores of Europe, the literature on famine in Latin America is dominated by northeastern Brazil. Here there are a number of contemporary, or near contemporary, accounts, like Herbert H. Smith, *Brazil, the Amazons and the Coast* (1879), to read alongside more scholarly works such as Reuben H. Brooks, 'Human Response to Recurrent Drought in Northeastern Brazil', *Professional Geographer*, XXIII, 1971; Rolando V. Garcia and Pierre Spitz, *Drought and Man*, volume 3 (1986); Anthony L. Hall, *Drought and Irrigation in*

North-east Brazil (1978); T. Lynn Smith, *Brazil: People and Institutions* (1946).

Until the last few decades, probably more was written about famine in Asia than in any other continent. Famine remains a frequent point of reference in many books on China: few fail to make some mention of it. For the nature and context of famine before the revolution of 1911, see Albert Chan, *The Glory and Fall of the Ming Dynasty* (1982); Harold C. Hinton, *The Grain Tribute System of China (1845–1911)*; Ping-ti Ho, *Studies on the Population of China, 1368–1953* (1959); Alexander Hosie, 'Droughts in China, A. D. 620 to 1643', *Journal of the North China Branch of the Royal Asiatic Society*, XII, 1878; Kung-chuan Hsiao, *Rural China: Imperial Control in the Nineteenth Century* (1960); Dwight H. Perkins, *Agricultural Development in China, 1368–1968* (1969); and the symposium in *Journal of Asian Studies*, XLI, 1982. C. Martin Wilbur, *Slavery in China during the Former Han Dynasty, 206 B.C.–A.D. 25* (1943) is another reminder of the ancient connection between famine and slavery. For famine in modern times, and especially its importance to western thinking about China, see Paul Richard Bohr, *Famine in China and the Missionary: Timothy Richard as Relief Administrator and Advocate of National Reform, 1876–1884* (1972); David and Isabel Crook, *Revolution in a Chinese Village: Ten Mile Inn* (1959); Raymond Dawson, *The Chinese Chameleon: An Analysis of European Conceptions of Chinese Civilization* (1967); Walter H. Mallory, *China: Land of Famine* (1926); R. H. Tawney, *Land and Labour in China* (1932); and Theodore H. White and Annalee Jacoby, *Thunder out of China* (1947).

Japan's experience of famine has been discussed in several recent studies, among them William Wayne Farris, *Population, Disease and Land in Early Japan, 645–900* (1985); Mikiso Hane, *Peasants, Rebels and Outcastes: The Underside of Modern Japan* (1982); Susan B. Hanley and Kozo Yamamura, *Economic and Demographic Change in Pre-Industrial Japan, 1600–1868* (1977).

India, another 'land of famine' in western eyes, has been the subject of a voluminous literature, including a vast quantity of nineteenth century eye-witness accounts and official reports. Works of directly historical relevance include: Mohiuddin Alamagir, *Famine in South Asia: Political Economy of Mass Starvation* (1980); S. Ambirajan, *Classical Political Economy and British Policy in India* (1978); David Arnold, 'Famine in Peasant Consciousness and Peasant Action: Madras 1876–78', in R. Guha (ed.), *Subaltern Studies III* (1984); B. M. Bhatia, *Famines in India* (1963); Lance Brennan, Les Heathcote and Anton Lucas, 'The Causation of Famine: A Comparative Study of

Lombok and Bengal, 1891–1974', *South Asia*, VII, 1984; Paul R.
Greenough, *Prosperity and Misery in Modern Bengal: The Famine of
1943–1944* (1982); Irfan Habib, *The Agrarian System of Mughal India
(1556–1707)* (1963); Ira Klein, 'When the Rains Failed', *Indian
Economic and Social History Review*, XXII, 1984; A Loveday, *The
History and Economics of Indian Famines* (1914); Michelle Burge
McAlpin, *Subject to Famine: Food Crises and Economic Change in
Western India, 1860–1920* (1983); and Ian Stone, *Canal Irrigation in
British India* (1984).

The literature on Africa is also now very considerable and
increasingly rich from a historical viewpoint. Particularly valuable or
suggestive are: G. Jan van Apeldoorn, *Perspectives on Drought and
Famine in Nigeria* (1981); Nicole Ball, 'Understanding the Causes of
African Famine', *Journal of Modern African Studies*, XIV, 1976;
Clarke Brooke, 'The Heritage of Famine in Central Tanzania',
Tanzania Notes and Records, 67, 1967; David J. Campbell, 'Response
to Drought among Farmers and Herders in Southern Kajiado District,
Kenya', *Human Ecology*, 12, 1984; David J. Campbell and David D.
Trechter, 'Strategies for Coping with Food Consumption Shortage in
the Mandara Mountains Region of North Cameroon', *Social Science
and Medicine*, 16, 1982; A. R. W. Crosse-Upcott, 'Ngindo Famine
Subsistence', *Tanganyika Notes and Records*, 50, 1958; David Dalby,
R. J. Harrison Church and Fatima Bezzaz (eds), *Drought in Africa – 2*
(1977); Finn Fugelstad, 'La grande famine de 1931 dans l'Ouest
nigérien', *Revue française d'Histoire d'Outre-Mer*, LXI, 1974; Michael
H. Glantz (ed.), *Drought and Hunger in Africa* (1987); Polly Hill,
Population, Prosperity and Poverty: Rural Kano, 1900 and 1970 (1977);
Paul E. Lovejoy and Stephen Baier, 'The Desert-side Economy of the
Central Sudan', *International Journal of African Historical Studies*,
VIII, 1975; Suzanne Miers and Igor Kopytoff (eds), *Slavery in Africa:
Historical and Anthropological Perspectives* (1977) – a subject also
discussed in Claire C. Robertson and Martin A. Klein (eds), *Women
and Slavery in Africa* (1983); John U. Ogbu, 'Seasonal Hunger in
Tropical Africa as a Cultural Phenomenon', *Africa*, XLIII, 1973;
Richard Pankhurst, 'The Great Ethiopian Famine of 1882–1892',
Journal of the History of Medicine, XXI, 1966; André Salifou, 'When
History Repeats Itself: The Famine of 1931 in Niger', *African
Environment*, 1, 1975; *Savanna*, 2, 1973, special issue on 'Drought in
Africa'; Jean Suret-Canale, *French Colonialism in Tropical Africa,
1900–1945* (1971); Meredeth Turshen, *The Political Ecology of Disease
in Tanzania* (1984); Megan Vaughan, *The Story of an African Famine:
Gender and Famine in Twentieth-Century Malawi* (1987); Michael

Watts, *Silent Violence: Food, Famine and Peasantry in Northern Nigeria* (1983); and J. B. Webster, 'Noi! Noi! Famines as an Aid to Interlacustrine Chronology', in J. B. Webster (ed.), *Chronology, Migration and Drought in Interlacustrine Africa* (1979).

The development of the agrarian economy of the United States since the mid-nineteenth century and its implications for famine elsewhere can be traced through Fred A. Shannon, *The Farmer's Last Frontier: Agriculture, 1860–1897* (1961), Mitchel B. Wallerstein, *Food for War – Food for Peace: United States Food Aid in a Global Context* (1980) and William W. Murdoch, *The Poverty of Nations: The Political Economy of Hunger and Population* (1980). American attitudes towards famine in Russia are revealed in George S. Queen, 'American Famine Relief in the Russian Famine of 1891-1892', *Russian Review*, 14, 1955, and H. H. Fisher, *The Famine in Soviet Russia, 1919–1923: The Operations of the American Relief Administration* (1927). In addition to Paul Ehrlich's *The Population Bomb* (1971) and William and Paul Paddock, *Famine – 1975!*, theories of global hunger and 'triage' are represented in George R. Lucas and Thomas W. Ogletree (eds), *Lifeboat Ethics: The Moral Dilemmas of World Hunger* (1976). Susan George *How the Other Half Dies: The Real Reasons for World Hunger* (1976, revised 1986), as well as being historically informative, is also undoubtedly one of the best introductions to the causes of contemporary Third World poverty and hunger.

Index

abortion, 36, 128, 129
Africa, 119, 128; agriculture in, 51, 86, 124; famine in, 1, 4, 23, 24, 26, 30, 33, 34, 49, 87, 88, 91, 92, 120-2, 124-5, 131; population of, 124
Agricultural Revolution, 66, 69
Ambirajan, S., 112, 126
Appleby, Andrew, 130
Asia, famines in, 1, 4, 124, 136
Aurangzeb, 99
Ausubel, Herman, 115
Aykroyd, W. R., 74
Aztecs, 119, 120

Ball, Nicole, 33
Bangladesh, 7, 20
Bengal, 89, 119, 120; agriculture in, 53, 68; famine (1769-70), 20, 110; (1943-4), 6, 12, 20, 22, 23, 27, 43-4, 45, 46, 68, 80, 82, 87, 89, 92, 97-8, 117
Bengal Famine Commission, 27, 43, 74, 86, 89
Bernier, François, 119
Bhatia, B. M., 81, 82
Bhils, 77
Biafra, 73, 97
Bihar, 73, 140
Black Death, 10, 25, 37, 69
Bohr, Paul, 100
Bois, Guy, 7
Bolshevism, 138-9
Book of Orders, 96, 106
Boserup, Ester, 41-2, 53, 63, 65, 86
Braudel, Fernand, 9, 105

Brazil, 30, 47, 72, 128; famine (1825), 21; (1877-8), 13-14, 21, 25, 77-8, 79, 93
Bright, John, 116
Buck, Pearl S., 16
Buckle, H. T., 130, 131
Bushmen, 49

Calcutta, 27, 44, 74, 89, 91, 92, 97
cannibalism, 16, 19
Ceará, 21, 93
Charlemagne, 106
Chaunu, Pierre, 64
Chesneaux, Jean, 11
China, 7, 16, 60, 85, 91, 123, 128; Communist revolution (1949), 65, 104, 120; famine in, 2, 14, 20, 21, 22, 24, 30, 38, 42, 64-6, 68, 78, 79, 84, 91, 92, 102-4, 120, 131, 132, 134, 135; famine (1876-9), 19, 20, 21, 22, 45, 103, 133, 136, 137; (1928-31), 21; (1958-61), 20, 104; peasants in, 50, 53, 58, 61, 64-5, 101-3; revolution (1911), 14, 66, 103; western images of, 119-20
cholera, 22, 24, 25, 26
Christian missions, 78, 134, 136; in China, 133-5
climate, 29-34
Cobb, Richard, 45-6, 107
Condorcet, Marquis de, 35
Confucianism, 100, 101, 103
Corn Laws, 70, 96, 106, 109, 112